THE
WORLD
WE
LIVE IN

VOLUME TWO

SPECIAL FAMILY EDITION

THE WORLD WE LIVE IN

by the Editorial Staff of

LIFE

and Lincoln Barnett

TIME INCORPORATED • NEW YORK

ON THE COVER: One of the mightiest of mammals was the woolly mammoth, which ruled the North American plains a million years ago, and whose tusks have provided half the world's ivory (*page 130*).

CONTENTS

LIFE MAGAZINE

The World We Live In was produced
under the general direction of
EDWARD K. THOMPSON, *Editor*
PHILIP H. WOOTTON, JR., *Executive Editor*
JOSEPH KASTNER, *Copy Editor*
by the following editorial staff:

Editor
KENNETH MacLEISH
Art Director
CHARLES TUDOR
Writer
LINCOLN BARNETT
Chief of Research
MARIAN A. MacPHAIL

Text and Picture Research by
NANCY GENET, DAVID BERGAMINI, WARREN YOUNG,
MARION STEINMANN, JAMES GOODE, PATRICIA GRAVES,
ROBERT CAMPBELL, ELEANOR PARISH, TERRY HARNAN

Paintings by
RUDOLPH F. ZALLINGER, CHESLEY BONESTELL,
RUDOLF FREUND, JAMES LEWICKI, ANTONIO PETRUCCELLI,
JAMES PERRY WILSON and ROBERT GARTLAND, SIMON GRECO,
WALTER LINSENMAIER, RICHARD EDES HARRISON

Photographs by
FRITZ GORO, ALFRED EISENSTAEDT, GJON MILI,
ANDREAS FEININGER, LOOMIS DEAN, ROMAN VISHNIAC,
J. R. EYERMAN
(The names of other photographers whose pictures appear
in this book will be found in the Picture Credits.)

This Special Family Edition of *The World We Live In,*
in three volumes, is an adaptation of the
original edition, published in one volume in 1955.

THE AGE
OF MAMMALS

PART VI

THE MAMMALS TAKE

D URING 100 million years of the Mesozoic era when dinosaurs ruled the earth, a group of small creatures dwelt amid the shadows of the swamps and sought safety in the branches of the forests. They represented a new class of animals, the mammals, warm-blooded vertebrates that bore their young alive and gave them milk in infancy. Never numerous—they have brought to the modern world only 3,500 species as against 8,600 bird species and 800,000 species of insects—they now encompass the largest and most intelligent of all terrestrial fauna.

Beholding the bewildering diversity of living things that populate the lands and waters of the world, man has uneasily recognized both his basic differences from other creatures and his kinship with them. Since the dawn of reason he has repeatedly defined and redefined himself both as a participant and spectator in the pageant of life. In the Christian view man is both flesh and spirit. To the modern naturalist he is *"Homo faber"*—a tool-making animal. To the psychologist he is a talking animal, capable of feeling guilt. But to the evolutionist man is essentially a mammal with an oversized brain.

This specialized organ, seat of the peculiarly human attribute of reason, is a heritage from the ancient past, born of uncompromising demands imposed on man's remote forebears in their fight for survival during the tyranny of the dinosaurs. Unlike the reptiles, which abandoned their young to circumstance, the mammals cared for their offspring in infancy, providing them with a period of education and experience. Those with the highest capacity for learning emerged best equipped for survival. Therefore, through natural selection, the mammalian brain enlarged rapidly. Moreover, unlike the dinosaurs, the mammals were endowed with heat control and an even body temperature and could resist climatic variations and sustain physical effort over longer periods of time.

So for millions of years the mammals lived in perilous coexistence with the dinosaurs. Four groups of primitive mammals have been identified as early as the Jurassic period, 165 million years ago; all must have descended from ancestral forms which evolved from therapsid reptiles in the late Triassic. It was not until the Cretaceous period, however, that the mammalian line began to burgeon. And then, with what seems incredible swiftness, the dinosaurs died and the shy and humble mammals came into a great inheritance—the entire face of the land.

The period of time since the mammals took over the earth is called the Cenozoic era. It is divided into seven epochs beginning with the Paleocene, 75 million years ago, and coming down to the Recent which is the epoch in which we now live. The story of the mammals during all these periods but the last is depicted chronologically in the painting shown in sections on the following pages, as it is preserved in the bone beds of America's West.

DOMINANT ANIMALS of the Cenozoic era are shown above in chronological order, from *Barylambda* (*bottom*) to woolly mammoth (*top*). The epochs in which they lived are indicated by the rock strata at right.

OVER THE EARTH

GIGANTOCAMELUS

MEGACAMELUS

PROCAMELUS

POËBROTHERIUM

PROTYLOPUS

TETRACLAENODON

PLEISTOCENE
1 MILLION
YEARS AGO

PLIOCENE
10 MILLION
YEARS AGO

MIOCENE
30 MILLION
YEARS AGO

OLIGOCENE
40 MILLION
YEARS AGO

EOCENE
60 MILLION
YEARS AGO

PALEOCENE
75 MILLION
YEARS AGO

A. Petrucelli

CAMEL'S PROGRESS is reconstructed above from skulls (*right*) found in layers of rock covering six epochs of the Cenozoic. Beginning with a primitive herbivore of the Paleocene (lowest stratum), camels evolved in western America until they mysteriously died out after the Pleistocene (dark brown areas at the top). In the Old World camels have survived into the seventh Cenozoic epoch, the Recent, in which we live.

PSITTACOTHERIUM   PLANETETHERIUM   ALLIGATOR PLANETETHERIUM
PLESIADAPIS   BOA CONSTRICTOR TAENIOLABIS   PRODIACODON SOFT-SHELLED TURTLE

Morning of the Mammals' Reign

AT the dawn of the Paleocene epoch only a few minor strains of the mighty dynasty of reptiles survived from the Devonian: alligators, turtles, and certain snakes and lizards. And the mammals that had clung to existence in the shadow of the dinosaurs were uniformly small and sequestered. In western America, which is depicted in the painting above, the shallow sea that had covered most of the great plains withdrew and the Rockies arose. The climate remained bland. Subtropical plants—figs, breadfruit, palmettos—bloomed across the wilderness.

Among the first mammals to descend from the trees were a few insect-eaters, insignificant in stature but vastly important in the evolutionary story, for they were the stock from which all true mammals of the modern world would eventually evolve. Their unimpressive prototype was *Prodiacodon,* a primitive hedgehog; more specialized members of the same group included *Planetetherium,* a

LOXOLOPHUS   PANTOLAMBDA   BARYLAMBDA

PALAEORYCTES   TETRACLAENODON   THYLACODON   MIOCLAENUS

gliding animal, and shrewlike *Palaeoryctes.* With them came the herbivore, *Psittacotherium,* and two survivors from the Mesozoic, ungainly *Taeniolabis,* whose tribe died out in the next epoch, and the marsupial *Thylacodon,* whose progeny persists in the opossums.

As the Paleocene progressed there emerged several lines of great future significance. Notable among these were the first primates, small arboreal, nocturnal animals like the long-tailed *Plesiadapis.* One of the first carnivores was *Loxolophus,* a small raccoonlike creature with sharp-cusped teeth. The group of herbivores represented by *Tetraclaenodon* and *Mioclaenus,* horse-headed, feline-bodied animals, was probably ancestral to the ungulates (hoofed animals) of today. Later in the Paleocene there appeared an order of truly hoofed vegetarians known as amblypods, or "slow-footed ones," among them sheep-sized *Pantolambda* and larger *Barylambda.* By the close of the Paleocene the land once more teemed with flourishing forms that ultimately would produce the most vigorous and efficient animals that ever trod the earth.

121

NOTHARCTUS OXYAENA PHENACODUS CORYPHODON PALAEOSYOPS
TETONIUS PARAMYS EOHIPPUS

An Epoch of Uncertainty

IN the 20 million years of the Eocene, nature indulged the evolving mammalian lines. The lowlands lay carpeted in subtropical green and upon them new orders appeared, the ancestral forms of most modern mammals.

At some time early in the Eocene, North and South America were sundered by the sea. As a consequence several primitive mammals thrived in isolation in the south while their kin died out in the north. Among the short-lived northerners were *Metacheiromys,* whose South American cousins survive today in armadillos, anteaters and sloths. The early primates—like *Notharctus* and *Tetonius*—also disappeared from North America, leaving the continent empty of primates until the arrival of man.

The rodents, like the small squirrelish *Paramys,* were more successful and began to diverge into the varied ro-

TRITEMNODON   DIATRYMA   EOBASILEUS   UINTATHERIUM

MESONYX   EOHIPPUS   METACHEIROMYS   HYRACHYUS

dents of today. The carnivores also continued to specialize, producing catlike *Oxyaena,* doglike *Mesonyx* and weasellike *Tritemnodon.* The ungulates specialized less successfully, fabricating such awkward creatures as *Phenacodus* and *Coryphodon.* More grotesque were the uintatheres, which grew into the awkward giants *Eobasileus* and *Uintatherium,* both of which shortly died out.

The extinction of the primitive herbivores may have been effected by the advent of modern ungulates. *Eohip-*

pus, the first horse, stood no higher than a fox terrier, yet its slender legs and even teeth made it a far more felicitous form than its lumbering precursors. With *Eohippus* appeared the titanothere *Palaeosyops,* and *Hyrachyus,* a forebear of modern rhinos. Among the mammals of the Eocene there also stalked a giant running bird, *Diatryma.* Diatryma's appearance suggests that at this moment of evolutionary history two growing dynasties, the birds and mammals, were locked in a struggle for sovereignty.

HERD OF OREODON

ARCHAEOTHERIUM

BRONTOPS

RABBIT

MESOHIPPUS

A Time of Trial and Triumph

OF all the epochs of the Cenozoic era none brought greater events than the Oligocene. Within its span the earth assumed many of the aspects it wears today. The Alps and the Himalayas rose skyward and in the American Northwest volcanoes spewed fire and ash. Meanwhile the climate grew cooler and in the heartland of America the ancient subtropical forests began to retreat southward, surrendering their dominions to grasses, conifers and hardwood trees.

The Oligocene also saw the fading away of most of the primitive mammals and the founding of the modern faunas. Of the earliest mammalian lines only a few lingered on. However, the order of rodents enlarged rapidly while ahead of them raced their relatives, the rabbits, which had begun to develop at the end of the Eocene.

The protagonists of the new epoch, however, were larger animals. The giants of the Oligocene were the

PROTOCERAS   HOPLOPHONEUS   PROTAPIRUS   POËBROTHERIUM

HYAENODON   SUBHYRACODON   BOTHRIODON

titanotheres, ponderous plant-eaters like the *Brontops,* a hoofed and horned beast, 14 feet long. Of the primitive flesh-eaters only *Hyaenodon* and his close kin survived, but two great modern groups of carnivores, the dogs and the cats, began to emerge. The cats were already notably represented by the saber-toothed *Hoplophoneus.*

The hoofed vegetarians had earlier evolved along two major lines: odd-toed ungulates (which now include horses and zebras) and even-toed ungulates (sheep, pigs, deer). Within the former group the horse continued to evolve with the *Mesohippus.* Other odd-toed ungulates were the first tapir, *Protapirus,* and one of the first true rhinoceroses, *Subhyracodon.* Concurrently the even-toed ungulates brought forth an ugly giant pig, *Archaeotherium;* an amphibious swine, *Bothriodon;* a gregarious ruminant, *Oreodon;* a deerlike cud-chewer, *Protoceras;* and an ancestral camel, *Poëbrotherium.* Thus as the Oligocene drew to its close the hosts of the herbivores and carnivores were already hastening down their diverse evolutionary corridors into the domains they occupy today.

DICERATHERIUM
PROMERYCOCHOERUS   MERYCOCHOERUS

Period of Plains-Dwelling

THE most momentous phenomenon of the Miocene was the sudden spreading of the grasses, which, having slumbered in the shade of the old subtropical forests, swiftly responded to the ever cooler, drier climate and seized vast areas of land. From their harsh, stubbly blades evolved today's basic cereals. As the grasses spread across the flatlands of America the grazing mammals ranged in ever larger herds, and numerous forest dwellers emerged from the green shadows onto the golden sunlit plains.

Under these conditions both branches of the ungulates expanded rapidly. By the end of the Miocene, the primitive horse *Merychippus* had developed hoofs and was adapted to life on the range. His odd-toed cousins, the rhinos and chalicotheres, were less successful. For a time, *Diceratherium,* a small but prolific rhinoceros, appeared to thrive, but in the next epoch he, along with all other rhinos, vanished from the American plains. Still swifter

MOROPUS   MACHAIRODUS

MOROPUS   DINOHYUS

HERD OF MERYCHIPPUS

SYNDYOCERAS

extinction overtook the chalicothere *Moropus,* a claw-footed caricature of a horse.

Meanwhile the even-toed ungulates assumed numerical ascendancy over their odd-toed competitors. Three genera of ruminants flourished briefly and then died out. Of these *Promerycochoerus* and *Merycochoerus* were amphibious; the third, *Merychyus,* was a plains dweller. The pig complex produced a Miocene giant, *Dinohyus,* the largest of all nonamphibious swine. The camels put forth two models: *Procamelus,* slightly larger than a

sheep, and *Alticamelus,* an outlandish sort of super-camel with a giraffelike neck. Deerlike ruminants also tried several experiments. The line initiated in the preceding epoch by *Protoceras* continued in the Miocene with *Syndyoceras,* an overspecialized creature burdened with two sets of horns. A more successful conception was tiny, horned *Merycodus.* A Miocene forebear of true deer and giraffes was graceful *Cranioceras.*

As in other ages the affluence of herbivores brought opulence to the flesh-eaters who preyed upon them. The

127

TERATORNIS

MASTODON   WOOLLY MAMMOTH   TERATORNIS

CASTOROIDES   MUSK OX

other end of the scale loomed *Teleoceras,* an immense amphibious rhino that had migrated from Asia during the Miocene and all but supplanted his indigenous American cousins. The second-generation mastodons had adjusted well to their new environment and produced several native genera, among them *Amebelodon,* a "shovel tusker," whose lower jaw extruded two long scooplike incisors ideally suited for dredging roots from soft earth.

The canine-ursine line also essayed gigantism: *Agriotherium* was an enormous bear, fully four feet high at the

shoulder; *Amphicyon* was a huge dog who doubtless dominated all other canine carnivores. Among the hoofed animals appeared *Sphenophalos,* a sturdy pronghorn, and *Synthetoceras,* culmination of the *Protoceras* line and the closest facsimile of a unicorn that nature ever contrived. The evolving horse entered the homestretch with the advent of *Pliohippus,* the immediate and virtually full-grown forebear of *Equus,* the genus man exploits today.

The transition from Pliocene to Pleistocene marked one of the great crises in the history of life. The ice sheets

130

TELEOCERAS   HERD OF PROCAMELUS   SPHENOPHALOS   SYNTHETOCERAS   PLIOHIPPUS

AMEBELODON   PLIOHIPPUS

EPIGAULUS   AGRIOTHERIUM   AMPHICYON   RABBIT

The Ages of Giants and Ice

THE Pliocene, which ended one million years ago, was the autumn of the Cenozoic era, the last lenient epoch before the invasion of the cruel ice sheets from the north. Little by little the winds grew sharper. Over the wide prairies of North America the tall grasses surrendered to shorter, hardier herbage. In the Southwest the subtropical forests shriveled in the rain shadow of the newly reared coastal Sierra, and then vanished under desert sands. Northward, pines marched down the slopes of the resurgent Rockies and young Cascades, out across the high plateaus, driving the sequoias from all but their present sanctuary in the California hills.

For the most part Pliocene life remained rich and variegated, and the evolving mammals continued to increase in size. Even the rodents prospered, begetting *Epigaulus,* who was notable not only as a giant among midgets but as the only member of his breed to grow horns. At the

MERYCHYUS   GOMPHOTHERIUM   CRANIOCERA
PROCAMELUS   ALTICAMELUS   MERYCODUS

weasel family diversified into many branches—the weasels themselves, martens, fishers, wolverines, skunks and otters. Raccoons and bears appeared, offshoots of the primal dogs. And on the wide plains large cats like *Machairodus* waited in the grass for their quarry.

Some 20 million years ago there appeared a stranger from the far side of the world. *Gomphotherium* the mastodon had come out of the valley of the Nile. In the late Oligocene his tribe made their exodus from Africa and headed eastward on one of the greatest pilgrimages in the history of living things. For millennium after millennium they stamped across southern Asia to the Pacific and then northward to the Arctic Sea. At the Bering Strait they found a land bridge temporarily emergent; they crossed it and entered the New World.

Thus at the end of the Miocene the plains of America teemed with life, more luxuriant than ever would thrive again after the coming of man. But the climate was growing colder; the ice caps were beginning to form. Soon their chill breath would be felt on the happy plains.

FOLD OUT, DO NOT TEAR

CRASSIOCORNIS   SABER-TOOTHED TIGER   EQUUS   MEGATHERIUM   MYLODON
CANIS DIRUS   BOREOSTRACON

overlying Greenland, Siberia and northern Europe now began to thicken rapidly. And as they grew, accumulating and compacting the snows of innumerable winters, the oceans fell. The Isthmus of Panama rose again from the depths and the land bridge across the Bering Straits lay completely dry. Across these great transoceanic causeways the animals of three continents streamed in increasing numbers, intermingling, interbreeding, waging an internecine struggle to survive. An immediate consequence was the all but total extermination of the archaic herbi-

vores and marsupials that had thrived in happy isolation in South America since the Paleocene.

During the first 100,000 years of the Pleistocene the ice sheets crept ever southward, refrigerating a third of the earth's surface. Then they receded and temperate climates again prevailed. Four times in all, the continental glaciers crunched down from the north, and four times they withdrew. (The latest retreat, which began some 10,-000 years ago, is still continuing today.) As they ground across the great plains, abrading the face of the land,

131

carving valleys and creating new lakes and rivers, the animals responded with tremendous vitality.

Notable among them were *Castoroides,* a beaver the size of a small bear; *Canis dirus,* a six-foot-long wolf; *Smilodon,* the saber-toothed tiger, whose jaws, capable of a 90° gape, were armed with six-inch fangs; and *Teratornis,* a carrion-eating cousin of the modern condor with a wingspread of 12 feet, the largest flying bird in the history of life. There were also giants among the ungulates—*Bison crassiocornis* and the durable musk ox which still persists in the Arctic today. The horse reached the climax of his evolutionary growth with *Equus,* only to die out in America at the end of the epoch.

The mightiest of all the Pleistocene mammals were the mastodons and mammoths. The latter, recent arrivals from Asia, swiftly came to rule the American plains, diversifying into at least four species, of which one, the 10-foot-high woolly mammoth, ranged the top of the world, dwelling among the glaciers. Among the immigrants from the south there arrived three prodigies: *Boreostracon,* a giant glyptodont, offshoot of the armadillo line; and the ground sloths *Mylodon* and *Megatherium.* The latter, one of the largest mammals that ever lived, weighed more than a modern elephant.

Unfathomably these great giants of the Pleistocene— the mammoths, mastodons, saber-tooths and sloths— died out as swiftly as the dinosaurs before them. As spring returned after the million-year-long winter, they vanished, leaving the reaches of North America to the small animals and the bison. All the largest and strongest animals of the Cenozoic era disappeared from the temperate zones of both hemispheres. Only tropical Africa and Asia somehow escaped the wholesale extinctions.

The great dying of the late Pleistocene and early Recent epochs marked the most far-flung and radically destructive crisis in the entire history of the mammals. To the evolutionist it presents an enigma no less baffling than the great dying of the reptiles 75 million years before, and as in the earlier instance he can only suggest multiple causes —climatic changes, competition, failure to adapt.

It is one of the striking configurations of evolutionary history that in each age some group of animals has risen from obscure beginnings to a period of ascendancy, only to surrender its sway to another incipient and apparently unaggressive line. Evolutionists hesitate to assign specific causes to specific extinctions, preferring rather to state simply that over great periods of time the physical environment changes and certain populations die off because for some reason they fail to adapt. The apparent suddenness and simultaneity of the great extinctions, moreover, may be an illusion created either by gaps in the chronicle of the rocks or by the immense perspectives of geologic time. Thus the great dying of the Pleistocene mammals was sudden only in a relative sense. It would appear that the extinctions occurred sporadically, spreading gradually from local centers, and were as often as not partial, wiping out faunas in one place and leaving them untouched in another.

As in earlier ages, the vitality of animal life proved greater than the destructive power of whatever forces had combined to imperil it. At the moment the sheer mass of life on the planet stands close to an all-time high, and, more significant, its diversity is greater than in any age prior to the dawn of the Cenozoic. For the major pattern of the evolutionary panorama is *divergence,* the tendency of life to differentiate, to become more variegated, to educe more and more forms and varieties of organisms ingeniously adapted to every conceivable habitat.

It is true that divergence is not the only configuration woven in the long tapestry of life on earth. Around it lie other patterns: static lines of arrested development (like the unchanging opossum, oyster, rabbit and turtle), forms of *parallel* evolution, where allied groups follow independent avenues of development and arrive at similar results (as in the case of deer and antelope); and forms of *convergent* evolution, where utterly unrelated groups change slowly into near facsimiles of one another (as in the case of the reptile ichthyosaurs and the mammal porpoises).

From the network of natural forces it is difficult to select a single strand representing a main line of progression, of advance to a propitious end. Yet, as the life saga has unfolded, it would appear that the factor most conducive to survival has been an increase in perception— the development of more efficient sense organs and more complex and sensitive nervous systems, capable of interpreting sensations and responding to them swiftly. From the beginning these attributes have constituted the great arsenal of the mammals.

It is probable that the mammals may have survived and succeeded to hegemony of the earth not in spite of but by reason of their very weakness and obscurity, their smallness in a world dominated by giants, their nakedness in a world of armor plate—in particular, by their fear and sensitivity and awareness in a world of unperceiving, insensate, brainless brutes. And as the epochs of the Cenozoic flowed past, these priceless endowments were augmented in certain lines through the elaboration of nervous systems and enlargement of brains.

The culmination of the present evolutionary progression is man. Proud of his intellectual equipment and of his sense of immortality, man has often tended to underestimate his other legacies—to envisage himself as a puny, hairless, wingless, shivering, unarmored, slow-footed pygmy in an arena of superior physical specimens, and to attribute all conquests to his rational faculties. Actually *Homo sapiens* is a giant in the animal kingdom; only a handful of mammalian lines are larger, stronger, swifter.

Of the more than one million species of animals on earth man is capable of killing all but a few without recourse to the weapons he ingeniously contrives for his own destruction. Yet it is true that man's supreme heritage is his brain—that mysterious and convoluted mass of soft tissue which enables him to perceive the world around him with unique acuity and respond to its stimuli with a subtlety and self-consciousness that sets him apart from all other living things. It invests him, moreover, with a power which no other creature ever possessed—the power to modify his environment, to govern and alter the very course of evolution for all the multifarious estates of life, including his own.

CREATURES OF THE SEA

PART VII

CREATURES OF THE SEA

THE sea abides, of all realms of life, the least known, the least explored, the largest and the darkest. Dropping to depths of nearly six miles, it encompasses about 300 times the habitable space of land and fresh-water areas combined. And most of it is a domain of everlasting night. Hence man knows far less of the ocean's creatures than of the animals with which he shares the land.

Yet the frontiers of marine biology have advanced in recent years and can provide some glimpses now not only of the populations that subsist in shallow waters, but of those that dwell below the glistening surface layers of light, in the canyons of the continental slopes and amid the oozes of the abyssal floor. And one can say that the most gigantic creatures that ever existed on earth wage war still in the oceanic deeps. With them too abide some of the loveliest forms the hand of nature has ever wrought, sculptured with silvery grace and symmetry, tinted with iridescent jewellike hues, shining sometimes with magic luminescence in the night.

Since the sea is the ancestral home of all living things, the creatures that inhabit it embody an animate panorama of evolution from the dawn of existence. All the main divisions (phyla) of the animal kingdom appear in the sea, as well as all their component classes—save only amphibians, birds, insects and true spiders. From bacteria and protozoans up to the most highly evolved of aquatic organisms, true fish and marine mammals, the long procession of life unfolds in the sea with a clarity and detail that have no parallel among the faunas of the land. For the sea has many living fossils—animals for whom the ages have stood still. Eon after eon, jellyfish, corals, glass sponges, starfish, sand dollars, horseshoe crabs, clams and other forms have reproduced their kind, virtually untouched by the slow sorcery of time.

At the moment of earth history when the first plants and animals climbed from the seas onto the dry land, the invertebrates were lords of creation. Single-celled protozoans drifted in the surface waters. Jellyfish shimmered through the upper layers. Mollusks and arthropods ruled the sunless sea floor. Sluggish, even sedentary, many of these bottom dwellers had no need or ability to swim. And so the middle reaches of the open sea lay almost empty for millions of years.

But in the lakes and rivers of the continents a new class of life was evolving—the fishes, which may have sprung from a special group of fresh-water invertebrates and learned to swim from the need to escape enemies and maintain their balance in swift-running streams. Their contours became more streamlined, their fins more flexible; they developed movable jaws and specialized teeth suited to a predatory life. In time they branched into two sub-classes: the cartilaginous fish, like sharks, skates, rays, whose skeletons are made of cartilage rather than bone; and the bony fish, the dynasty of cod, herring, salmon, tuna, mackerel and other true fish (teleosts) of the present day. Sometime in the late Devonian and Triassic periods the ancestral vertebrate fish came down to the sea, and finding the ability to swim a distinct advantage among the slow, crawling communities of the salt water, survived, thrived and improved their unique mode of locomotion. Today the teleosts with over 20,000 species are the common fish of the sea.

Since the sea is a more homogeneous environment than the land, its creatures are generally more primitive, less diversified than land creatures. By and large they have not had to adapt themselves to such contrasting habitats as deserts and swamps, jungles and grassy plains, nor to endure extreme climatic variations. Even in the tropics the temperature of the surface waters seldom exceeds 85°; in polar regions it never falls much below 29°. Over more than three quarters of the ocean's surface the seasonal temperature variation is less than 5°; below 800 feet there is no seasonal change at all.

Moreover the water in which aquatic creatures live sustains them against the relentless tug of gravity. Unlike land animals which require solid supports to undergird them in the thin medium of air, marine organisms in the denser medium of water have no need for heavy legs or hard internal frames. Sea plants have no trunks or rigid stems. The limbs of most sea animals are designed for swimming, digging or fighting rather than support. This is true even of the great whales, whose bones are spongy and filled with oil. Indeed a whale, though an air-breathing mammal, quickly dies if washed ashore, its lungs crushed by the weight of its own vast body.

Yet despite the homogeneity of the marine environment, the absence of impassable deserts and of unscalable mountains, the sea too has its barriers: invisible boundaries of temperature, salinity, pressure and light. Most sea creatures, having no regulator systems like those of land animals designed to protect them against sudden and intense environmental changes, are extremely sensitive to slight variations in their watery medium.

Thus temperature differences serve to confine marine life to certain regions of the sea. Many cold-water creatures of north and south latitudes are identical, yet differ sharply from tropical species that inhabit the seas between. Sudden shifts in ocean currents, bringing, for example, masses of warm water into regions occupied by cold-water creatures, may completely destroy the populations within vast areas. Similarly, a sudden change in salinity, caused perhaps by the disgorging of flooded rivers into coastal waters, may destroy oysters and other inshore invertebrates. Pressure too imposes horizontal boundaries between layers of the sea. Although some fish reveal an amazing ability to move from one pressure

AMID CORAL SPIRES in a world of rippled sand and swaying plumes, monstrous and magnificent creatures glide. Here a grouper, goggle-eyed and heavy-jowled, hangs above the sunlit ocean floor. He is a member of that class of streamlined, neckless, water-breathing vertebrate animals called fish, the best known to man of all the thousands of kinds of creatures that inhabit the far-flung dominions of the teeming sea.

THE CROWDED SEA teems with schools of fish. Some species are solitary hunters like marlin, barracudas and sharks. But many more, like these Australian Caesios, incorrectly called kingfish, travel together in great numbers, possibly for mutual protection, possibly in response to some deep instinct. The precision with which such schools swim in formation, twisting, diving, accelerating in unison with their leaders, never

level to another without harm—and whales are capable of plunging to 3,000 feet or more—most sea creatures remain between certain self-imposed strata marking the upper and lower limits of their abode.

A more obdurate barrier is light—not because vision is the most important sense to the majority of marine organisms, but because sunlight is indispensable to the aquatic plants that compose the basic food supply of the sea. All plants obtain their nourishment by converting inorganic substances—water, carbon dioxide and certain minerals and salts—into food. The process by which they do this, called photosynthesis, depends entirely on the sun's energy. So plants in the ocean are confined to the sunlit upper waters; none grows below 250 feet.

Nowhere beneath the waters is there vegetation comparable to the thick forests of the land. Marine plants are primitive, rootless, trunkless, usually small, and limited in kind. There are only a few seed plants—such as eel grass and surf grass. The rest consist of the seaweeds, of minute blue-green algae and of the single-celled plants called diatoms. The latter, though microscopic in size, reproduce faster than any terrestrial flora, often doubling in number every second day and in a year producing many tons per acre of open water. In spring and fall the surface of the sea turns yellow, brown and green as the diatoms bloom, and they lure hordes of sea creatures to their enormous pastures. Where the diatoms flourish, there too flourish the world's great fisheries—along the west coasts of North and South America, in the North Sea, off Portugal, Japan and Newfoundland.

And so the sea is a diversified domain, divided, like the land, into many provinces and precincts, each with

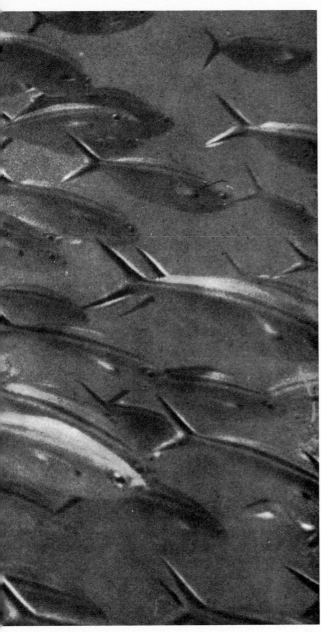

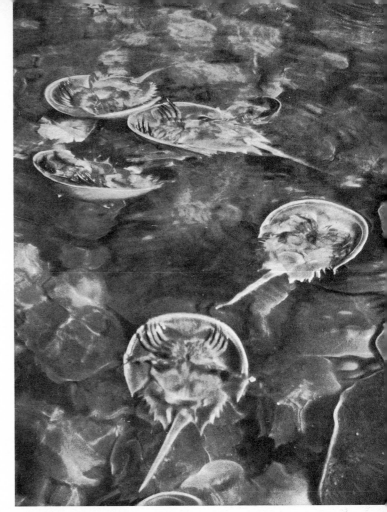

THE SUPPORTING SEA enables marine creatures to float with little effort. Here horseshoe crabs float on the surface on their backs, using legs as oars. They can also swim right side up or crawl on the bottom.

colliding, remains a mystery of nature comparable to that presented by the formation flying of birds. Whether they maneuver chiefly by sight, sound or response to the "backwash" of the lead fish, no one can say.

its own populations and ways of life, separated one from another by unseen environmental walls. From the perspective of marine biology the sea encompasses two great dominions: the pelagic environment (open water) and the benthic environment (the bottom). And each of these in turn embraces several separate and distinct categories of life. Pelagic life is divided into plankton (floating creatures that have little power of locomotion and drift with the currents) and nekton (free-swimming creatures of all kinds). Benthic life exists all the way from the littoral benthos (the inshore bottom) downward to the abyssal benthos (the deep sea floor out beyond the continental slopes). Though drowned in a common medium and interpenetrated by the ever-restless currents of the deep, each of these great domains of life is nevertheless a world of its own, shaped by disparate circumstance.

THE FERTILE SEA provides hanging gardens of sea plants as pasturage. Here a halfbeak skims under a patch of Sargassum in the Caribbean. Its long lower jaw is designed for snatching food from below.

137

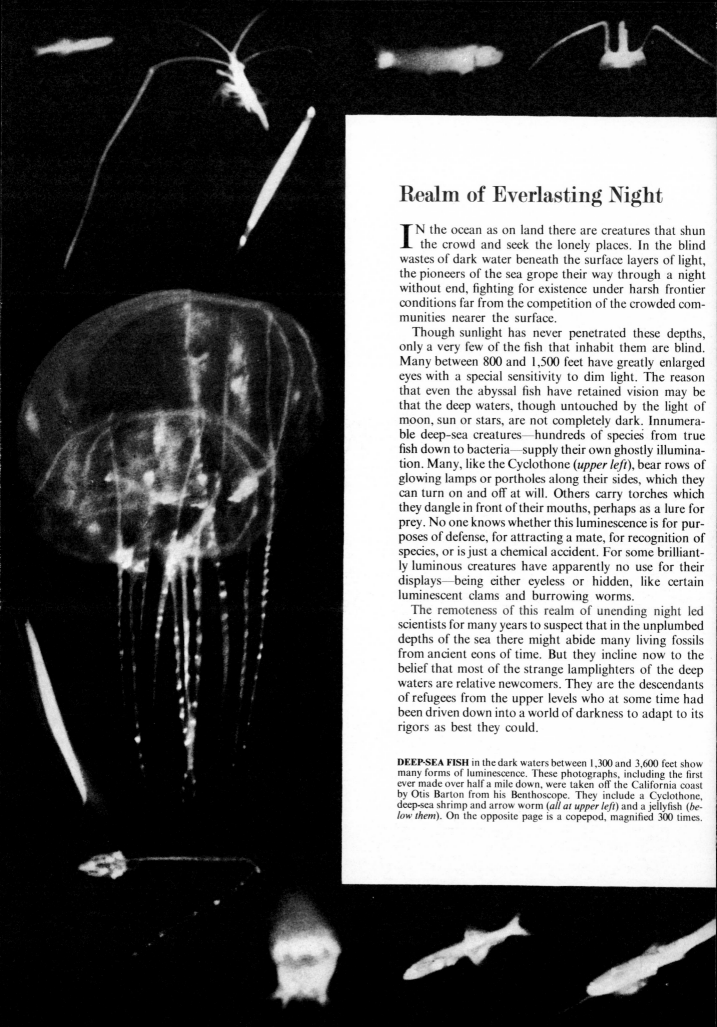

Realm of Everlasting Night

IN the ocean as on land there are creatures that shun the crowd and seek the lonely places. In the blind wastes of dark water beneath the surface layers of light, the pioneers of the sea grope their way through a night without end, fighting for existence under harsh frontier conditions far from the competition of the crowded communities nearer the surface.

Though sunlight has never penetrated these depths, only a very few of the fish that inhabit them are blind. Many between 800 and 1,500 feet have greatly enlarged eyes with a special sensitivity to dim light. The reason that even the abyssal fish have retained vision may be that the deep waters, though untouched by the light of moon, sun or stars, are not completely dark. Innumerable deep-sea creatures—hundreds of species from true fish down to bacteria—supply their own ghostly illumination. Many, like the Cyclothone (*upper left*), bear rows of glowing lamps or portholes along their sides, which they can turn on and off at will. Others carry torches which they dangle in front of their mouths, perhaps as a lure for prey. No one knows whether this luminescence is for purposes of defense, for attracting a mate, for recognition of species, or is just a chemical accident. For some brilliantly luminous creatures have apparently no use for their displays—being either eyeless or hidden, like certain luminescent clams and burrowing worms.

The remoteness of this realm of unending night led scientists for many years to suspect that in the unplumbed depths of the sea there might abide many living fossils from ancient eons of time. But they incline now to the belief that most of the strange lamplighters of the deep waters are relative newcomers. They are the descendants of refugees from the upper levels who at some time had been driven down into a world of darkness to adapt to its rigors as best they could.

DEEP-SEA FISH in the dark waters between 1,300 and 3,600 feet show many forms of luminescence. These photographs, including the first ever made over half a mile down, were taken off the California coast by Otis Barton from his Benthoscope. They include a Cyclothone, deep-sea shrimp and arrow worm (*all at upper left*) and a jellyfish (*below them*). On the opposite page is a copepod, magnified 300 times.

Free Swimmers of the Open Sea

UNLIKE bottom dwellers, bound to the ocean floor, the free-swimming creatures of the sea move buoyantly through a three-dimensional world in which mobility, keen senses and protective coloration are the means of survival. From the blue upper layers of the water to its lightless depths, ocean life varies in form, abundance and habit with its level in the many-storied sea.

The open waters are the kingdom of vertebrate fish, though they share their sovereignty with some invertebrates, like the giant squid, and the mightiest of mammals, the whales. The aristocrats among them—the swiftest and the handsomest—hunt near the surface where there is more food.

Their speed kings are the blue marlin, capable of spurts up to 50 mph; the sailfish; the dolphin; and the dolphin's favorite prey, the flying fish, which taxis at 35 mph and soars rather than flies through the air. Not much slower are the tuna and the oceanic bonito. Sharks, largest of all fish, are the wolves of the sea. A near kin of the shark is the harmless manta or devilfish, which may attain a weight of 3,000 pounds and, like a sailfish, often leaps from the water, falling back with a splash resounding for miles.

Most of these surface-dwelling fish have been tinted by nature to blend with their glimmering en-

vironment. Since the long wavelengths of sunlight are absorbed in the upper 75 feet of water, the dominant undersea colors are green, blue and violet. These persist feebly to 2,000 feet in clear waters (like those shown from the surface to 4,000 feet in the composite painting at right).

Pelagic creatures of the upper stories of the sea tend to be bluish on top and silver underneath. From about 600 to 1,500 feet, a twilight grayish zone, the fish are correspondingly light-hued—like the silvery *Sternoptyx*, *Diretmus* and *Opisthoproctus*. Below, in the zone of utter blackness, animals display the brown and black shades of *Melanocetus* and *Photostomias*, though a few, such as the scarlet deep-sea prawns, astonishingly wear bright colors for reasons no one can guess.

Indeed, the little known about deep-sea creatures has been deduced from the occasional specimens brought up in the nets of marine biologists. Many of them are represented among the curious forms shown at right. But the fact that most deep-sea fish are equipped with enormous gaping mouths and long, needlelike teeth is suggestive of the bitter struggle to survive in the blind depths where food is located by chance. One such fish, *Chiasmodon*, has a distensible stomach that enables it to swallow prey somewhat larger than itself.

But the greatest battles of the oceanic deep are waged a quarter mile down by the sperm whale and its ancient prey, the giant squid.

SEA COLANDER
PHYLLARIA DERMATODEA SEAWEED

SEA GRAPES

EDIBLE MUSSELS
PINK-HEARTED HYDROIDS
REDBEARD SPONGE   OYSTER DRILLS
RIBBED MUSSELS   ROCK BARNACLES
IRISH MOSS

COMMON STARFISH
RAZOR CLAM SHELL

SEA VASES

SEA ANEMONE, RETRACTED
SEA PORK
SUN STAR
MOON SNAIL SHELL
BOAT SHELL

DOG WHELKS
PERIWINKLES
PURPLE STARFISH
CORALLINE ALGAE
BLOOD STARFISH

SAND DOLLAR AND SHELL   SEA PEACHES
MUD STAR
BRITTLE STAR

MUSSEL SHELL

The Bottom Dwellers

AMID the weedy gardens of the inshore shallows, life flourishes as in no other region of the sea. Here upon the benthos, on the pallid sands and mud, a multitude of sluggish creatures subsists in a strange, slow-motion world. The very quality of existence seems more akin to the kingdom of plants than to that of the swift, darting fish, and many benthic creatures resemble plants in outer aspect and have plantlike names: sea anemones, sea cucumbers, sea peaches, sea grapes. Yet they are animals—members of the vast empire of soft-bodied invertebrates, engineered by nature for life on the ocean floor.

The foundation on which the whole edifice of benthic life depends is the rich supply of minerals dissolved in

CKWEED   ROCKWEED   KELP

SEA ANEMONE   TORTOISE-SHELL LIMPETS

ROCK CRAB   SOFT CORAL

JINGLE SHELLS   GREEN CRAB   SEA CUCUMBER   CLATHRIA DELICATA SPONGE

EEN SEA URCHIN AND SHELL   WHELK EGG CASE   BLUE CRAB   EYED FINGER SPONGE

SEA ANEMONE, EXPANDED   SKATE EGG CAPSULE

HERMIT CRAB IN BORROWED SHELL   PURPLE SEA URCHIN   LADY CRAB   YOUNG HORSESHOE CRAB

Y SCALLOP SHELL

the water and stored on the ocean floor. To most marine life calcium is a crucial element, but especially to soft-bodied benthic creatures whose hard outer coverings not only protect them against predators and the pounding of the surf, but also provide anchorage for the muscles with which they dig and crawl.

The bottom minerals are also important to the plant life which flourishes in the sea gardens of rockweed, kelp and Irish moss that adorn the coastal shelves. Though rootless, many seaweeds anchor themselves to rocks or sand by threadlike "holdfasts" or flat disks. If their anchorage is deep, they may grow stems up to 100 feet long so that their main foliage can float in sunlight, buoyed up by little self-contained bulbs of gas. The largest seaweeds are the kelps, flat brown plants that anchor in rocky areas offshore, beyond the zone of the crashing surf.

SEA SQUIRTS often cluster in colonies on rocks and pilings. They feed by pumping water in and out of their digestive cavities via two body orifices. When alarmed they squirt water from both.

Lazy Hunters in the Deep

FOR many creatures of the sea, the water in which they dwell provides a rich chowder, filled with an abundance of food particles which they need only strain out and ingest. On the bottom there is detritus—a kind of slime composed of decaying matter and the bacteria that break it down—as well as swarms of protozoans, tiny worms, larval forms and other small organisms. So most bottom dwellers live engulfed in food and have little more to do than open their mouths, if they have mouths.

Sponges and sea squirts anchor themselves to rocks or other solid objects and feed by pumping detritus-laden water in and out of their bodies. Oysters and clams are also pumpers and spend their entire adult lives in beds. A few livelier organisms make somewhat more of an effort. Barnacles, for example, catch food particles in the bristles of their outstretched hairy legs which intermittently draw in the haul like seining nets. Sea cucumbers snuffle along the sea floor like vacuum cleaners, using their tentacles to shovel slime into their mouths. Their rate of movement is slow; some make 18 inches a day.

STINGING TENTACLES of a sea anemone paralyze a small fish. Spiral bands around each tentacle contain small poisoned "needles." When the prey is immobilized, it is drawn into the mouth.

THE SEA ANEMONE resembles a flower but is a carnivorous three-inch animal able to catch, kill and digest fairly large prey. Its basal end is a disk with which it clings to rocks or glides slowly across the sea floor.

THE FILE SHELL is the most active of the bivalves. A relative of the scallop, it has tentacles which are sensitive to taste and touch. It gets its food by straining water through scarlet, sheetlike gills.

SERPENT STARS are carnivores, scavengers which crawl along, mouth downward, searching for mollusks and feeding on slime. If one is cut in two, each half will regenerate a complete animal.

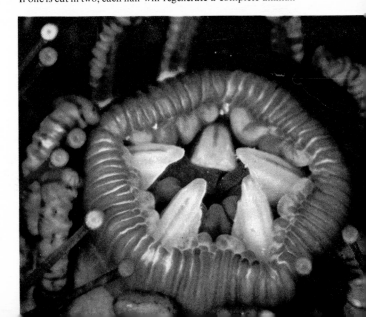

THE SEA URCHIN (*right*) has a voracious-looking mouth on its underside, which is armed with five efficient "teeth" able to crush small mollusks, to cut up sea lettuce (a seaweed) or to scrape algae off the rocks.

A BOXING SHRIMP fights off larger fishes. Though only about an inch long and almost transparent, this delicate tropical creature courageously rears up on its spindly legs and, raising its enlarged fore-arms, armed with strong pincers, repels would-be predators with right and left jabs and uppercuts. Its sensitive antennae and the sensory hairs on its legs enable it to detect the approach both of danger and of food.

Arts of Defense and Camouflage

THE open sea offers little sanctuary comparable to the woods and thickets of the land, and so, to survive, each species has had to evolve its own weapons and defenses. To some, like the tuna, shark and barracuda, have gone the implements of sheer power—sharp teeth, swift reflexes, speed and strength. To others—for example, the oyster, snail and clam—have gone shells or armor plate.

But marine creatures have developed other unique and highly specialized defenses. Squid, octopi and some kinds of shrimp blind their enemies by a discharge of "ink." The sting cells of jellyfish and anemones contain coiled, hollow darts which, when triggered, inject a paralyzing poison. Sting rays carry poisoned spines on their tails;

HIDING FISH lurk among the tentacles of a sea anemone. Safe from its sting, these damselfish live in harmony with their dangerous host. They attract larger fish which the anemone kills. Then they share the feast.

A SQUIRTING SEA HARE defends itself by ejecting "ink." The animal, a mollusk, is named for its long earlike "antennae." A related mollusk provided the "Tyrian purple" dye which the ancient Phoenicians used.

A SLASHING SAWFISH defends itself with great flailing strokes of its serrated proboscis, which is equipped with two rows of 25 to 29 bony "teeth." No kin to the swordfish or marlin, the sawfish inhabits warm, shallow waters of the Atlantic and Pacific. It descends suddenly on a school of smaller fish, hacking them to pieces before they escape. Then at leisure it eats up the mangled victims that have fallen to the sea floor.

other rays and some eels are equipped with electric organs capable of administering a severe shock. Sponges have minute spikes that lodge in the enemy. And certain sea cucumbers, in moments of extreme peril, eviscerate themselves, and, leaving their internal organs behind to distract the foe, slip away and grow new ones.

Many creatures that dwell upon the sand and in the coastal shallows imitate their environment. Flatfish and rockfish change color in accordance with the color of their background. Decorator crabs cement bits of seaweed over their shells and legs. The hermit crab, which has a tender rump, adorns it with discarded shells. Some sea urchins become covered with snails so they look like snail colonies. Finally, a small animal may attach itself to a larger one for security—as in the case of the shark sucker, and the barnacles on the head of a whale.

A CAMOUFLAGED PIPEFISH poises among blades of eelgrass off the California coast, hardly distinguishable from them in appearance. Its long snout is adapted to probing for the small crustaceans it preys on.

A BRISTLING BLOWFISH of the coral seas inflates itself with water, thus becoming too big for most of its foes to swallow. At the same time it erects the forbidding-looking spines that normally lie flat on its body.

147

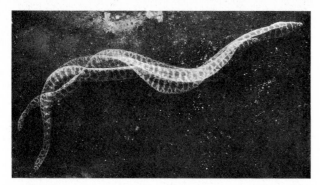

UNDULATING its body, a reef-dwelling moray eel, in repetitive flash photograph, advances somewhat as a snake wriggles. A moray is a true fish. Its suppleness enables it to slither into rock crannies for prey.

Arts of Locomotion

THE populations of the sea have evolved many techniques and aids to locomotion—streamlining, jet propulsion and varied rhythms of movement. Since the density of water is virtually the same as that of its inhabitants, they have little difficulty staying afloat. Yet even the smallest of marine creatures are not entirely free from the tug of gravity, and for this reason many are endowed with special mechanisms to keep them suspended. Most fish have air sacs; others are honeycombed with oil deposits or swaddled in thick layers of fat.

Not all creatures of the sea are fish, however, nor do all of them swim. Planktonic forms for the most part simply drift with the wandering currents, and bottom dwellers are mostly either ambulatory—crawling like crabs and lobsters or gliding like snails and anemones, or sedentary—like oysters, sponges, barnacles and corals, which anchor themselves to the ocean floor. The truly accomplished swimmers of the sea are fish and marine mammals.

For most fish, their fins serve less as implements of propulsion than as stabilizers, ailerons, rudders and brakes. Their main propellant is body movement, augmented by pushing action from the tail or extrusion of water from the gills. The movements range in degree from the undulation of the eel's whole body to the restricted action of the armored boxfish, which can move only its tiny fins and tail. Fish probably navigate partly by eyesight, partly by hearing, partly by tactile sense and partly by smell. Although they have no external ears, their auditory sense

DARTING through the water like torpedoes, speedy porpoises travel in spurts up to 25 mph, often leaping from the water in graceful, arching bounds. Since they are air-breathing mammals they must surface fre-

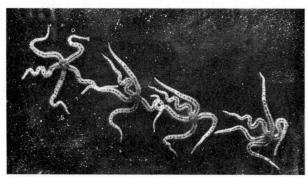

CREEPING, a Caribbean brittle star, shown in repetitive flash photograph, pulls itself along with two arms and shoves with the other three. It is far more agile than its stiff-armed cousin, the common starfish.

JET-PROPELLED, an octopus has a muscular mantle which it fills with water. This is then extruded through a funnel, which can be turned in any direction. On the bottom an octopus crawls on its tentacles.

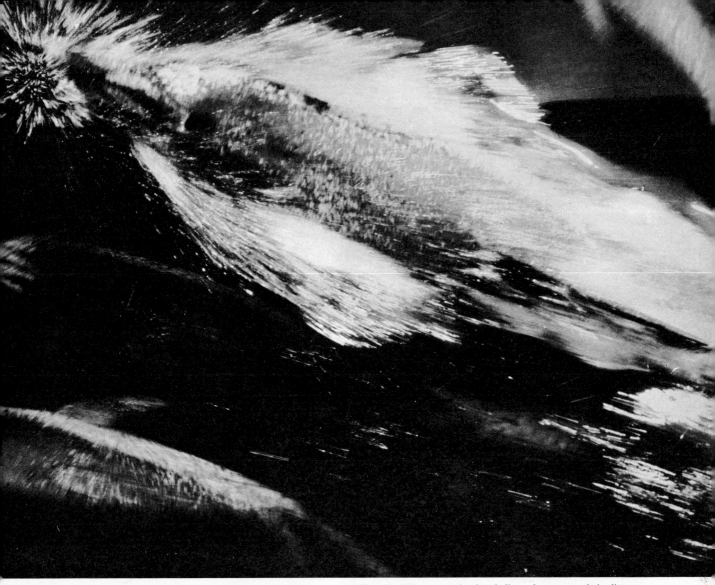

quently, sucking air through a blowhole on top of their heads, which is visible above in the porpoise just bursting the surface. The holes close with amazing rapidity when they dive. Although porpoises have excellent eyesight, some scientists believe they gauge their distance from solid objects by emitting sonic and supersonic noises and computing their position from the time of the echo, as bats do in the air.

JUMPING, a file shell escapes enemies by clapping its shells together like castanets. Ejected water stirs up a small cloud of sand and debris and may carry the creature a few feet from its point of take-off.

WALKING, a West Indian batfish resembles a land animal. Its fins not only look and walk like legs but support the batfish when it rests on the ocean floor. In swimming, it uses its tail as a propellant.

149

AN EAGLE RAY flies like some great bird of prey through a school of sheepshead, flapping its winglike pectoral fins. It also uses its "wings" to agitate the sand in quest of mollusks. In one night a ray may dig a ditch as wide as its 4-foot wingspread, a foot deep and 20 feet long. As it digs it scoops up clams and crushes them between its rows of flat teeth. It ranges the Atlantic from tropical waters north to Cape Cod.

is highly developed. They maintain equilibrium through small organs called statocysts. These are cavities lined with sensory hairs and containing some loose objects such as small grains of sand, which give them an indication, even in the utter blackness of the abyss, whether they are upright or upside down.

One of the mysteries of marine biology is just how fish manage to sleep, for they have no eyelids and, like air-planes, have to keep in motion to keep from falling. A few flat, benthic fish, notably flounders, soles, skates and rays, often lie down on the bottom mud and sands. Others wedge themselves in crevices for the night. Small pelagic types occasionally appear to bask among drifting seaweeds. But so far as the free swimmers of the open waters are concerned no one can say how they sleep, or indeed if they ever sleep at all.

A GREEN TURTLE uses its slender front flippers as oars and its rear limbs as steering apparatus and kickers. On dry land it moves ponderously and without grace, crawling along the warm Atlantic beaches to which it must return periodically to lay eggs. Of all the marine reptiles of the Mesozoic era, the turtle tribe almost alone has survived to the present day. A few small sea snakes also persist in parts of the Pacific.

SEA SLUGS or nudibranchs, which are mollusks without shells, move about by sliding along on a muscular foot. They often crawl upside down while grazing on hydroids (*above*). If disturbed they lower themselves to the ocean floor at the end of an almost invisible thread of slime anchored to the hydroid, or, if in open water, to the surface film. Sea slugs nibble off the heads of hydroids, which then grow new heads.

PLANKTON specimens are illustrated above, most of them many times magnified, although the bell-like medusa at bottom above is actually two inches long. They include: a diatom (*straight yellow rod near center of right-hand page*); radiolarians and foraminifera (*small circular shells to left of diatom*); a dinoflagellate (*pick-shaped object in lower center of left-hand page*); a copepod (*above the dinoflagellate*); a

The Lush Pastures of the Sea

SPREAD across the oceans of earth is the diffuse aggregate of living things known as plankton—a floating community of thousands of species of plants and animals concentrated in the surface waters. Most are microscopic in size, but slightly larger forms are also included. The characteristic of plankton that sets it apart from other sea life is that its powers of locomotion are too feeble to compete with the moving currents. Its name, from the Greek word *planktos*, means "wandering."

Plankton is the prime food supply of the sea. In the sea as on land the animal kingdom depends on the plant kingdom for food. All sea life is dependent ultimately on the single-celled microscopic plants called diatoms, which constitute six tenths of planktonic material.

In addition to diatoms, plankton includes incomputable numbers of protozoans—one-celled animals whose minute shells compose the oozes that blanket vast areas

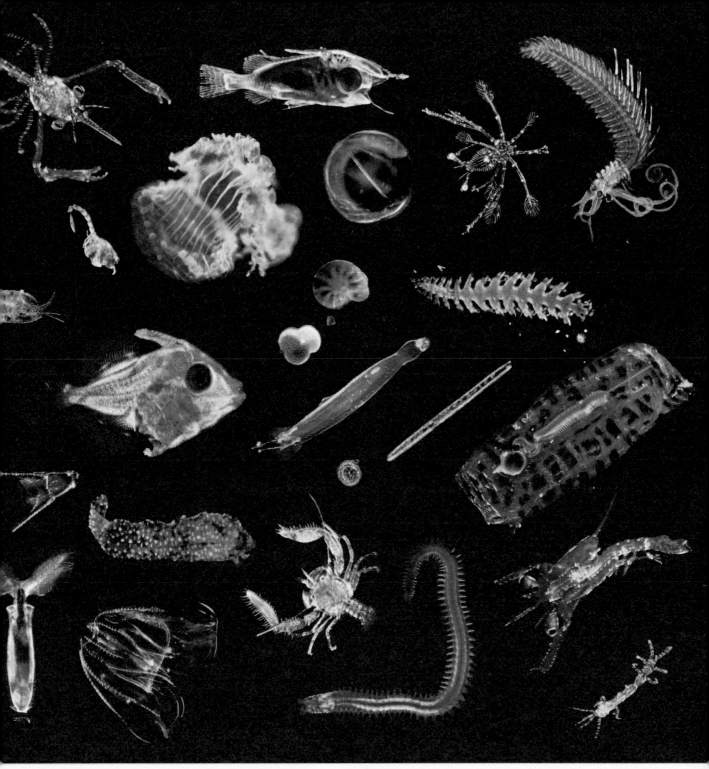

shrimplike mysid (*to right of copepod*); a "flying" snail (*top, center of left-hand page*); sea worms, one with egg sacs (*near upper left-hand corner*) and one with tentacles (*upper right-hand corner*); sea "spiders" (*left-hand page, center right and upper right corner*); young fishes (*right-hand page, left center and top center*); larvae of sea urchin (*V-shape below fish*) and spiny lobster (*near tentacled worm, top right*).

of the ocean floor—and the equally prolific dinoflagellates, half plant, half animal, whose transparent bodies give forth a ghostly luminescence. Along with these ride numberless intermediate forms—tiny arthropods, such as copepods and mysids; the larvae of sea urchins, snails and lobsters; sea worms and sea "spiders"; and many kinds of baby fish, together with a few larger floating forms such as jellyfish and Portuguese men-of-war.

Some of these creatures do move about within a small range. Each dawn the planktonic animals descend to avoid the light of day; each evening at dusk they rise again. This daily vertical migration is probably at least in part the source of one of the mysteries of oceanography—the "scattering layer" that reflects sound echoes within a fluctuating range of 300 to 1,500 feet.

Wherever the teeming pastures of plankton luxuriate, all forms of marine life abound. For plankton is the food factory of the sea, the start of the endless food cycle that sustains all creatures of the open waters, from sardines and herring to the titan of the oceans, the blue whale.

The Endless Chain of Food

VIRTUALLY every free-swimming creature lives on the flesh of others smaller than itself and represents a meal for others larger than itself. It is estimated that 10 pounds of food are required to build one pound of the animal that eats it. Thus it would take 10,000 pounds of diatoms to make 1,000 pounds of copepods to make 100 pounds of herring to make 10 pounds of mackerel to make one pound of tuna to make 1/10th pound of man.

The ocean's populations are involved in a never-ending cycle of eat and be eaten. Even when an animal dies, it is devoured by scavengers or decomposed by bacteria. Then it becomes detritus, and is either consumed again by detritus feeders or wafted aloft to provide fertilizer for the diatoms on the surface. And so the sea's food cycle is renewed, day after day and year after year.

COPEPOD EATS DIATOMS. Tiny copepods, pinhead-sized to a quarter of an inch, are among the world's important food animals. The sea's food cycle begins with their consumption of microscopic diatoms.

HERRING EATS COPEPODS. Diatom-fed copepods are a favorite food of the baby herring which sifts them through sievelike "rakers" in its gills. Once 60,895 copepods were counted inside a herring's stomach.

The herring group, which includes sardines, shad, menhaden and alewives, is considered the most valuable of all fish groups because of the abundance of food it supplies to other marine creatures and to man.

SQUID EATS HERRING. From one inch to over 50 feet long, all squid are carnivorous and predaceous, subsisting on fish, crustaceans and other mollusks. When a squid catches a fish in its tentacles, it draws the

fish toward its mouth, which has a horny, parrotlike beak; then it bites out big chunks which it gulps down. The eyes and brains of squid and octopi are among the most highly developed in the marine world.

BASS EATS SQUID. A sea bass grows to about 18 inches and perhaps six pounds. Its consumption of the squid that ate the herring that ate the copepod that ate the diatoms marks the penultimate stage of this particular food cycle. The ultimate stage may be reached when the bass is eaten by man. Or if it escapes predators and dies of other causes, its remains will sink to the bottom and be consumed by scavengers.

Life and Death in the Sea

THE sea is at once a vast cradle and graveyard of life, a nursery where incalculable hosts of visible and invisible creatures procreate, and a battleground wherein the chances of survival may be but one against 10 million of violent death. In the transition from egg to adult each creature must run a gantlet of ever larger enemies whose pursuit never ends (*pictures at right*).

Those that escape being eaten may succumb to starvation, to parasites or to immense catastrophes occasioned by storms, shifts in the currents or changes in the temperature or composition of the sea water. Recurrent "red tides" caused by an explosive increase of dinoflagellates, which consume vast quantities of oxygen and emit vast quantities of toxic wastes, from time to time annihilate fish life on a prodigious scale.

But if the sea is wasteful of life, it is also prodigal in its inception. The reproductive rate of marine creatures confounds the imagination of slow-breeding man. If every codfish egg laid in the sea ultimately grew into an adult, in six years the Atlantic Ocean would be packed solid with cod. A codfish may lay up to five million eggs at one time, an oyster 11 million, a sunfish 300 million. A sea hare lays eggs at the rate of 41,000 per minute, producing perhaps 500 million in a single season. If each one matured and reproduced for four generations, the resulting mass of sea hares would occupy a space about six times the volume of the planet Earth.

The exigencies of existence in the sea are such, however, that the miracle of marine life consists not so much in the profusion of eggs as in the fact that any survive at all. Only a few sea creatures care for either their eggs or their young. One that does is the octopus: the female broods over her clusters of eggs, stroking them and fanning the water around them with her tentacles to assure proper circulation. In most cases eggs are discharged freely into the water, there to drift with the currents or settle to the bottom and take their chances of escaping the numberless voracious predators, including their own parents, that wait to devour them. Yet the mechanisms of nature are so exquisitely adjusted that the average survival, for example, of only one oyster egg in half a billion is sufficient to preserve the balance between overpopulation and extinction of the species.

The development of an egg into a larva neither terminates the individual's hazards of survival nor greatly lessens its prospects of annihilation. For example, the eggs of one species of clam develop into free-swimming larvae one day after fertilization. Several days later, a larva that has escaped being eaten settles finally to the ocean floor where, if currents have swept it over an uncrowded area of bottom, it may dig into the sand or mud and there ultimately mature into an adult clam. But it may also drop down onto the parental bed where the older population may be clustered thickly—perhaps several adult clams to every square foot of surface—all busily pumping sea water in and out of their double-barreled syphons. There the baby clam may be sucked into the syphons of some kinsman and cannibalistically consumed.

The development of sea creatures from egg to adulthood may involve an interval of many years and the

IN SWIFT PURSUIT, a three-foot Caribbean octopus reaches for a blue crab, its favorite food. The crab first tries to bury itself in the sand, then darts away and temporarily escapes the octopus' lashing tentacles.

CAPTURED, the crab lies helpless in the octopus' grasp, already minus a joint which has been torn off by the octopus. If necessary the octopus might simply drop down and engulf the crab in its mantle like a tent.

DOOMED, the crab is drawn toward the octopus' mouth, which has a horny, pointed beak that is easily capable of crushing the crab's shell. But the octopus prefers to suck the crab's flesh slowly from its casing.

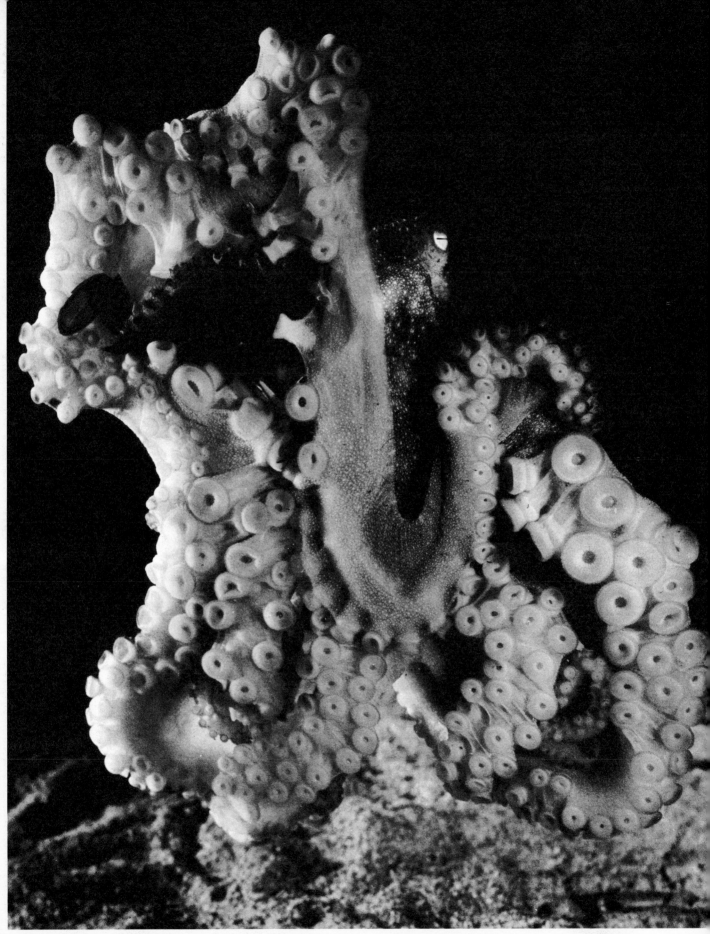

LINGERING OVER ITS REPAST, the octopus plucks the crabmeat from each joint with its beak while holding the crab with the powerful suction cups on its tentacles. In two hours the crab is only a hollow shell.

Reputedly dangerous to man, the octopus is actually a timid animal that flees at the approach of any swimmer. Various species range in diameter from one inch to almost 30 feet. All octopi have eight tentacles.

negotiation of many a sea mile from birthplace to final habitat. Many forms of both vertebrate and invertebrate life employ the restless currents to disperse and deploy the species. Some creatures cover tremendous distances during their early development. Perhaps the greatest of all instinctual migrations is that of the European eel.

Each autumn, in response to some mysterious urge, adult eels leave the fresh waters where they dwell and come down to the sea. Then, guided no one knows how, they find their way across almost 3,000 miles of the open Atlantic to their spawning grounds in the depths of the weed-strewn Sargasso Sea. It is here that their eggs are laid, and from here that the new-hatched eel larvae start their long journey home, sweeping with the great clockwise swirl of the Gulf Stream northward and eastward to the European shore. This immense journey takes the larvae three years. At its end, metamorphosed into elvers, they swim unerringly upstream into the rivers and lakes where they slowly develop into adult eels. About ten years later, reaching sexual maturity, they return to the sea, and head back to their remote Sargasso spawning grounds, there to reproduce and die. It is in these same far reaches of the sea that the American eels also engender their kind. Only for them the journey is shorter; the swing of the Gulf Stream carries the larvae back to the American coast in a matter of six months.

As mysterious as the ability of eels to navigate their way across the uncharted ocean is the response of other fish to the rhythm of the tides. The success of their spawning depends on a delicate calculation of the phases of the moon and the advance of the tidal flood.

Shortly after each full moon and each new moon between March and August hordes of silvery grunion appear in the surf off the California beaches. As the semimonthly high tide reaches its maximum and begins to ebb, the grunion ride ashore on the large waves. Glistening in the moonlight, they thrash around briefly on the wet sands, long enough for the female to extrude her eggs and the male to fertilize them. Then they fling themselves into an outgoing wave and are gone. Behind them, buried in the sand, the fertilized eggs lie safe from the hammering of the surf, because the tide is on the ebb and not for about two weeks will the alignment of sun, moon and earth produce another tidal peak. For a fortnight the eggs incubate in the warm sand. And then, when once again the waves break high on the beach, the eggs rupture, the baby fishlets emerge into the water and are borne out to sea on the breast of the outgoing tide.

And so it is not only by the extravagance of its reproductive processes but also by such exquisite adaptations to the environment of the sea that marine life sustains itself in the face of infinite dangers and the unceasing, implacable, internecine wars of kind against kind. Yet there is another thread that binds together the tapestry of life in the sea. That is longevity. No one knows how long fish, if spared from predators, starvation or disease, can live. But the age of some fish, like that of trees, may be read from annual growth rings formed in their scales, and there is evidence that certain fresh-water fish—carp,

GIVING BIRTH, a male seahorse bears down on a branch to expel one of more than 600 babies (*above*) from his brood pouch, where, days earlier, the female laid eggs. Below, he braces for another delivery.

catfish, pike—may live 100 years. Of the age of oceanic fish little is known. But one of the most provocative theories of modern biologists is that the process of aging is inextricably linked with the process of growth and begins only when growth comes to an end.

In the case of man and all terrestrial animals, the organism undergoes a definite period of growth during which the protoplasm, the actual living cells, continually divide and do not age. But when certain fixed dimensions are attained, growth terminates and the process of deterioration or aging begins. Although this does not apply to trees which may live for thousands of years, adding outer growth year after year until they succumb to disease, fire or the ax of man, it probably holds true for most land animals, because the tug of gravity imposes an outside limit on the size of moving bodies. Only a few terrestrial creatures ever exceeded the dimensions of the elephant and they are now extinct. But beside the 140-ton whale, the five-ton elephant is a dwarf, for the support of weight is no problem in the sea.

Some biologists believe that for aquatic animals, liberated from the destructive power of gravity by the dense medium in which they dwell, growth, though it may slacken almost to cessation, never halts entirely. So long as they escape—or are protected—from the primitive dangers of the sea, fish may therefore continue to grow by simple enlargement year after year. And so long as they continue to grow, according to this theory, they do not grow old. For them there is no old age, only the violent death that lurks everywhere in the world of waters. From this profound paradox of the sea there may sometime emerge new answers to the ultimate mysteries of life and death—for it was in the sea that life and death began.

From the sea too may some day arise a solution to the eternal problem of human hunger. The luxuriance of marine life is such that, in the opinion of some biologists, the earth's waters can never be utterly fished out. Every year man lifts more than 27 million tons of fish from the oceans without perceptibly affecting the population of any species. But even should a day arrive when the great fish dynasties begin to wane, the fructiferous sea holds other untouched riches.

The world's greatest potential source of food lies in the globe-encircling meadows of plankton with their multitudes of living creatures. The algae that sustain the planktonic communities may some day yield to us the nourishment they contain. The hosts of crustaceans, tiny fish and other animals that graze upon them represent an almost inexhaustible future harvest. And so in the end, man may turn again to his original home, seeking sustenance in what the Elizabethan playwright, Thomas Dekker, described as "that great fishpond, the sea."

THE
CORAL REEF

PART VIII

THE CORAL REEF

ON the periphery of the great wandering sphere on which man rides down the trackless avenues of space, there stand many edifices of nature—mountain ranges erected by paroxysms of the planetary crusts and sculpted by the slow, cold chisels of wind, frost and rain; canyons and gorges incised by running water and creeping ice; and oceanic deeps formed by forces in the earth's hot core. In addition to the general land forms, the patterns of rock and water that shape the visible world, the earth has many special areas of existence—windy plains, arid deserts, luxuriant forests. Of these none is more wonderful, none lovelier than the coral reef wrought not by blind physical agencies but by living creatures, diminutive in stature and primitive in form, yet master builders of the palaces of the sea.

Ever since European explorers began to rove the tropic oceans, the Western world has known of coral isles rising, palm-fringed and surf-ruffled, amid the blue desolation of the sea. Below the waters there loomed a fabulous world of living creatures, a glimmering realm of flowerlike animals, giant clams and gaudy fish with iridescent scales of gold and silver, ruby and emerald, glinting among the groves and grottoes of the coral gardens.

Until the last century, however, the nature of coral remained a mystery. Today it is generally known that the substance called coral is composed of the skeletons of innumerable small marine animals. Flourishing around the world in tropic waters, these tiny creatures are the creators of thousands of reefs, atolls and island festoons. No one knows precisely how much coral there is on earth, but it takes its place with the mineral substances of the planetary surface as one of the major architectural ingredients of the world in which man lives.

Owing to the blossomlike aspect of coral gardens, with their branching fronds, fans and clusters of infinitely variegated hues, corals were long mistaken for plants. Actually corals are members of the great phylum of the animal kingdom known as Coelenterata, which includes jellyfish, sea anemones and hydroids. An individual coral polyp consists of little more than a fleshy cylinder or tube, ridged inside with spokelike partitions. At the top is a mouth, bearded with tentacles, serving both as an inlet for food and an outlet for excreta, sperm and eggs; the other end, or pedal disk, is anchored to a limy cup which rests in turn on some solid object, generally the skeletons of dead ancestors. Voracious carnivores, corals feed on planktonic animals—young fish, tiny crustaceans, worms—which they catch and paralyze with their stinging tentacles.

Save for a brief, free-swimming larval stage, corals lead completely sedentary lives; as soon as they settle down, they start secreting lime, and quickly invest themselves in cuplike armor into which they retract for protection. As coral colonies grow, the feeding heads on the upper and outer fringes thrive at the expense of those beneath them, which slowly smother and die, leaving their empty skeletons as foundations for future progeny to build on. It is thus, by the never-ending labor of untold generations of small artisans, each in turn erecting its delicate castle, that the profuse coral islands, reefs and atolls of the earth's oceans have been reared.

Although coral grows in all the seas, the reef-builders exist only in shallow, sunlit, tropic waters—seldom more than 22° from the equator, and rarely at temperatures below 68° F. or at depths greater than 150 feet. Their requirements are rigorous. They must have clean water, for heavy mud and sediment quickly suffocate them. They must have sunlit water, for within the tissues of each coral polyp there exists a form of alga which, it is thought, provides oxygen and abets the excretory process of the coral, and which itself requires sunlight for photosynthesis. And finally they seem to demand restless, moving water, for only through the surge of waves and currents can sufficient oxygen and food be wafted within range of their tentacles—this explains why reefs are always best developed on their seaward side.

More than a century ago Charles Darwin observed that there appear to be three kinds of coral reefs: the fringing reef, which fans out from the edge of land in an almost solid shelf; the barrier reef, which is separated from land by a wide lagoon or channel, and the atoll, a coral ring enclosing a lagoon which stands in the open sea. Since coral grows only in the bright surface layers of water, one of the mysteries of atolls and barrier reefs, whose seaward ramparts often plunge to depths of thousands of feet, has been the nature of the foundations on which the original growth began.

The best answer to this riddle was suggested by Darwin himself and is accepted with a few revisions today: i.e., modern atolls and barrier reefs stand on a sunken basement of ancient fringing reefs that have been submerged either through the slow settling of the ocean floor or a rise in ocean levels. And as the land subsided, or the waters rose, the corals kept on growing upward toward the sun, outward toward the open sea. Final confirmation of Darwin's submergence theory came only recently from Eniwetok atoll, where drills bit downward through layer after layer of antique coral. Finally from a depth of 4,000 feet they brought up a core of volcanic rock—vestige of a long-vanished island on whose drowned flanks corals began to build untold ages ago and continued to build, generation after generation, fighting ever upward through the encroaching waters. The living corals of Eniwetok today bestride the summit of a mighty unseen tower, at once a catacomb of countless creatures long since dead and a monument to the continuity of life.

THE REEF BUILDERS, living coral polyps, twinkle their tentacles in lucent Bahamian waters like a field of stars. Only at night do coral gardens thus bloom, for corals are nocturnal feeders. In the day they fold their tentacles and shrink back into their stone mansions. In the middle of this coral colony is a familiar reef-dweller, a tubeworm, with its feathery gills partially expanded, waving like a peacock fan.

QUEEN

TOWNSVILLE

HINCHINBROOK IS

FLINDERS PASSAGE

MACKAY

BUNKER GROUP

CAPRICORN GROUP

WHITSUNDAY PASSAGE

SWAIN REEFS

N

South Pacific Ocean

THE WORLD'S BIGGEST CORAL REEF extends for 1,260 miles along the northeast coast of Australia from the Bunker Islands in the south (*left*) to the Murray Group near New Guinea in the north (*right*). The width of the channel or lagoon between the outer fringes of the reef and the mainland varies from about 100 miles near Swain Reefs to a minimum of seven miles. On the outer edges of the Barrier the coral

The Great Barrier Reef
of Australia

ACROSS the tropics of both hemispheres coral structures stud the encircling oceans. The mightiest of these and one of the supreme wonders of the world is the Great Barrier Reef, a great submarine buttress 1,260 miles long and 500 feet high, enclosing a watery domain of about 80,000 square miles off the northeastern coast of Australia. The greatest single edifice ever reared by living creatures, it dwarfs the works of man.

Owing to its remoteness, few people, even Australians, have ever seen this fabulous coral world. The pictures on these pages are therefore windows opening on one of the most remarkable and little-known regions of the planet. The Great Barrier Reef is not a solid wall, but rather a complex construction in which all three major categories of coral reef (*below*) are represented. In the south, where

BARRIER-TYPE REEF is disclosed by the surf crashing against its submerged coral cliffs. In this aerial photograph, the 600-foot-deep waters of the sea appear at left, the shallow waters of the channel at right.

AN ATOLL in the Capricorn Group exhibits the characteristic ringlike configuration of coral structures that have grown upward from the shores of sunken islands. Set back from the Barrier's outer edge, the

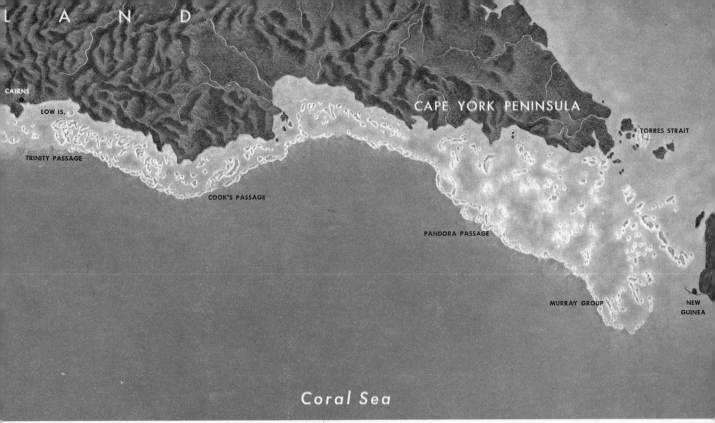

L A N D

CAIRNS

LOW IS.

TRINITY PASSAGE

CAPE YORK PENINSULA

TORRES STRAIT

COOK'S PASSAGE

PANDORA PASSAGE

MURRAY GROUP

NEW GUINEA

Coral Sea

walls fall away to depths as great as 8,000 feet. The waters of the lagoon are shallow and dotted with islands, atolls and uncharted coral outcroppings. The islands close to the mainland are the peaks of

the waters are cooler and inimical to coral growth, the Barrier is fragmented—a labyrinth of subsidiary reefs, coral sand bars, atolls and shoals separated by many wide channels. But northward, in warmer waters, the length of its component reefs increases and the channels between them diminish in number. For the northernmost 500 miles it presents an almost unbroken parapet, rising like an underwater mountain chain.

Although many parts of the Great Barrier are submerged at high tide and some never rise above the sur-

drowned hills and mountains of a submerged coastal plain. The clustered isles of the reef are almost all of coral construction, most of them uninhabited except by a few pearl fishermen and lighthouse keepers.

face at all, they effectively defend the inner lagoon from the violence of the ocean waves. Windward of the reef the waters are white with surf. To leeward, in the calm waters of the lagoon, coasting vessels pick their way amid the coral islands between Brisbane and Cape York. In wintertime antarctic whales enter the warm, still waters of the lagoon to bear their young.

At one time far in the geologic past the floor of this inland sea formed part of the Australian mainland, a flat coastal plain dotted with hills and low mountains. Then

atoll stands in less than 200 feet of water. From the windward side (*foreground*) surf foams over the parapet into the shallows of the lagoon. Within the leeward arc an island has been formed of coral sand.

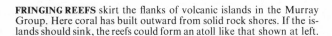

FRINGING REEFS skirt the flanks of volcanic islands in the Murray Group. Here coral has built outward from solid rock shores. If the islands should sink, the reefs could form an atoll like that shown at left.

STAGHORN CORALS are among the most prolific and most beautiful architects of the Great Barrier Reef. Their name comes from their antlerlike branches. They flourish on flat reefs, especially in sheltered waters. Slender, brittle as glass, staghorns are recurrently decimated by storms. After typhoons, their branches litter the weather side of reefs. Here a school of blue damselfish wanders in a staghorn grove.

these marginal lands began to settle, leaving only the crests of the coastal hills protruding above the waters: the inshore islands visible today. The warm shallows favored the growth of coral and, at a rate of perhaps three feet per 1,000 years, the coral grew as the coastal plains subsided and the ocean levels rose.

In the building of the Great Barrier, however, the corals have not labored alone. Here, as in every reef, other agencies were and are continually at work. The skeletons of the builders themselves are the main building blocks, but the whole structure is honeycombed with apertures which are filled with smaller units—tiny shells and other skeletal debris. Even so the structure might remain a loose mound of rubble, subject to disintegration by the sea, were it not for deposits of lime laid down by coralline algae. This mortar binds the reef together, cementing it into a solid rampart.

While the coral polyps are fabricating their houses, other forces are relentlessly at work tearing them down. The foremost destroyers are the ocean waves, beating on the seaward walls, forever driven by the Southeast Trades. Typhoons break up vast sections of the reef. There are also plant and animal enemies—sea urchins that rasp holes in the coral surface, boring mollusks and algae, and clams that wedge themselves into ever-deepening cavities. All these undermine the structure of the reef. As in every domain of nature, growth and destruction, life and death are forever in conflict.

In this never-ending battle the forces of creation have been consistently victorious. Along the entire length of

STAR CORAL SKELETONS mesh together like cogwheels in a part of the Great Barrier Reef. Star corals are among the most important reef makers. Below are the pipelike houses built by organ coral polyps.

A HUGE CLAM is wedged in the living corals of the reef. Largest of all bivalves, giant clams weigh up to 500 pounds, measure four feet across. Swimmers have drowned when their feet got caught in these shells.

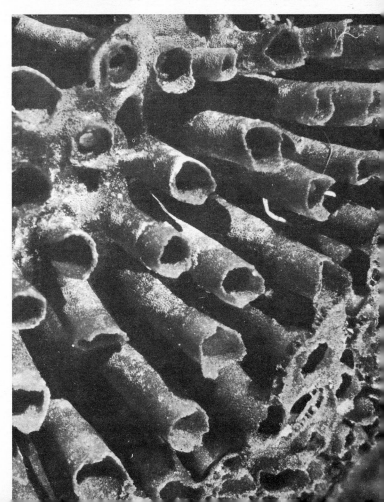

PANDANUS TREES weave a dense fabric of roots and branches on an island of the Great Barrier Reef. One of the commonest of coral island trees, the pandanus offers both food and shelter to the human residents of the reef, who pound its pineapple-shaped fruit into a kind of dough and weave its strong, supple leaves into walls and thatches. Its stilt roots provide support in the shifting sands in which it grows.

the Great Barrier the corals continue to build, consolidating their holdings and extending the reef area. In time it is possible that discontinuous units of the Barrier will fuse into a solid mass, for the living coral of today may become the coral island of tomorrow. As the skeletons of coral and other reef organisms disintegrate under the waves' attack, they crumble into sand which piles up in the leeward side of lagoons, forming beaches. In time the sands are cemented together by the lime produced by algae and become coral rock. Then vegetation is added, brought by bird droppings, by driftwood bearing seeds, by coconuts or by mangrove seedlings which wash ashore, still viable, and propagate their kind. Soon the bleak, tide-drowned reef has become a romantic "Summer isle of Eden lying in dark-purple spheres of sea."

Lovely as they loom from a distance, with their trees and white encircling necklaces of surf and sand, coral islands do not invariably present in close proximity the aspect of enchanted gardens. Their vegetation is often unruly, consisting in part of unkempt mangrove swamps with weird trees wading in a sodden ooze (*below*), and in drier sections of a nearly impenetrable jungle of pandanus trees (*left*), often interspersed with coconut palms, banyans, papaw trees and other vegetation. The mangroves, as unsightly as they are, perform an important role in island building, for their spreading roots collect debris and sediment which in time consolidate a higher soil base suitable for other trees and plants.

The most notable tenants of Barrier Reef isles are birds. In certain months multitudes of aquatic fowl dramatically converge on the Barrier islands to mate, build nests and rear their young. Sometimes to an observer on a ship at sea one of the islands appears to be overhung by a black, menacing cloud. On closer approach the cloud resolves into galaxies of soaring, wheeling birds—noddy

SPINY SEA URCHINS, armed with sharp barbs, thrive among mangrove roots. The round object in the center is a brain coral.

A MANGROVE TREE rises from the swampy waters of a Barrier Reef atoll. Growing in mud, the mangrove rises above the water on its tangled stilt roots which twine with roots sent down by the branches.

URCHIN FISH lurk for protection among a sea urchin's spines, maintaining their vertical position by movements of their fins.

NODDY TERNS congregate in vast numbers in the pisonia trees of the Barrier Reef isles. Their nests are rough structures of leaves, seaweed and grass. As many as 143 nests have been counted in a single tree.

A GREEN TURTLE digs a hole in the sand in preparation for egg-laying. First she digs until her shell is even with the surface of the beach. Then with her rear flippers she digs a deeper hole under her ovipositor.

terns (*left*), sooty terns (*below*), boobies or muttonbirds, or shearwaters. For most of the year these birds range the islands of the South Seas. But in season some instinct summons them to the Great Barrier Reef. One small coral island has a seasonal bird population of more than a million. During the breeding season the birds appear never to sleep. By day they fly out over the waters in quest of food. By night they make love, fight and feed their young, accompanying their domestic activities with eerie shrieks and screeches, groans and moans that earlier gave rise to a legend that the islands were haunted by condemned souls in torment.

The birds share their coral dominion with two other prolific populations: the soldier crabs and the giant green turtles. When the tide ebbs at night, the beaches come

SOOTY TERNS promenade the beach at Michaelmas Cay, a favorite breeding spot of aquatic birds. The entire island is one vast roost, teeming with terns, cluttered with nests, pervaded by the acrid odor of their droppings. Most active of the many species of birds that inhabit the islands of the Great Barrier Reef, the sooty tern is also known as the wide-awake, for it is on the wing all day, searching for small fish

SMALL TURTLE EGGS emerge rapidly until 100 or more have been laid. The mother turtle then covers them with sand. In a few weeks the young turtles hatch, head straight for the water and swim out to sea.

alive with armies of crabs out for food which scatter at dawn to dig burrows and escape their enemies, the birds. It is at night too that the giant green turtle comes ashore to spawn. Plodding up the beach in an undeviating line, the mother turtle climbs above the high-tide mark, digs a hole and lays her eggs (*above*). Then, covering them firmly and abandoning them to the contingencies of nature and circumstance, she returns to the sea. When the baby turtles hatch, they find themselves in a world of infinite peril. As they make their way instinctively toward the water, the sharp claws and murderous beaks of the larger birds may pluck them helpless from the sand, rending their tender shells. Those that escape this attack and reach the surf are still not secure, for hungry fish lie waiting for them in the insatiable sea.

A SOOTY TERN CHICK stands forlornly on the beach, waiting for its parents to return from a hunting trip. Tern chicks wear speckled brown and white plumage; the adult has black on its back, white on its belly.

and squid, and during the breeding season seems to be up all night, mating, fighting or caring for its vociferous young. What rest it gets probably consists of brief naps. Terns are monogamous, each male having but a single mate which lays but a single egg. However, so numerous are the eggs of the assembled sooty terns that the beaches of Michaelmas Cay are virtually covered with their white gleaming shells.

A CORAL RIDGE edges the outer barrier at Bikini atoll where the reef falls away into the depths. The seaward margin is coated with encrustations of purplish algae that protect the coral from the waves. Its edge (*right*) is grooved with surge channels, formed by irregular growth of the coral and sculptured by wave-erosion. Under water the reef shelves into terraces, then drops steeply and finally slopes to the deep floor.

The Teeming Underwater World of Reefs

THE preceding pages have described the structure, vegetation and animal populations of Australia's Great Barrier Reef. Beneath the surface of the water there lies another, far stranger domain, and it is in this submarine realm that all the coral reefs of the world become as one. Wherever in the world they exist, all coral reefs reveal certain basic structures in common. And whatever type they may represent—atolls, barrier reefs or fringing reefs —their tide-exposed flats resemble crumbly fields of multicolored stones, mirrored in small pools in which many forms of vertebrate and invertebrate life abound. Above the water at the seaward edges of the flats broad ridges stand (*above*), wrought by the pink algae that cover underlying coral with a veneerlike glaze. Serrating the ridges of many reefs are the surge channels through which the waves course and drain. At the outer edges of the ridges the coral cliffs drop away in slopes often steeper than those found in most mountains of the land. It is at the brink of these enormous ramparts that the fantastic blue underwater realm of the reef begins (*opposite page*).

AN ANCHOR WORM uncoils in the shallows of a coral flat. Amazingly, anchor worms can curl up into small blobs or stretch into thin tubes several feet long. They dwell among rotting coral and empty shells.

A MARINE SNAIL glides along the bottom of a tidal pool. It propels itself by means of a muscular foot, drinks through its trunklike syphon and scrapes up food with a rasplike tongue at the tip of a proboscis.

THE SUBMARINE FORESTS of a coral reef glow in the clear blue light that filters down from the surface. Here, 25 feet down in Bahamian waters, coral trees and shrubs, spires and boulders loom on every side.

Every type abounds: delicate, stone-hard staghorn corals (*right center*), sea whips and sea fans (*center*), round, corrugated brain corals (*upper left*), and encrusting cabbagelike Porites (*center foreground*).

KING CORAL, an Alcyonarian form, spreads its delicate branches above a school of butterfly fish in shoal waters off New Caledonia. The coral used by jewelers is a distantly related Mediterranean species.

STAGHORNS strain upward in the shallows off Nassau. At their base (*left to right*) are sea whips; a trumpet fish, swimming vertically; and a sea fan. Below are chimney sponges in Harrington Sound, Bermuda.

IN A CORAL GLADE Bermudian fish poise jewellike above the shrubs and blossoms of the shallow floor. At left a clump of crooked sea rods partially screen the waving tentacles of an anemone. In the right fore-

Artisans of the Reef

LIKE riotous gardens congealed into stone, coral reefs bear many varieties of blooms, charmed frozen flowers of every shape and hue. Exquisite branching trees and shrubs, fans and fronds rise from the beds and borders of the sunlit flats and cling to the ledges of the seaward cliffs as alpine blossoms cling to the rock gardens of the land.

But in addition to flowerlike forms, many other structures diversify the underwater world of coral. There are corals that look like toadstools and corals that resemble the cortex of the human brain, corals that form caves

ground a pink squirrel fish—so called because it chatters like a squirrel —nuzzles a cluster of Alcyonarian corals while an angel fish hovers overhead. Above the angel fish is a spotted chub. In the background a squad of sergeant-majors deploys. At the extreme right swims a blue-striped grunt, which gets its name because it grunts. Contrary to popular belief, many fish make noises; the sea is not a silent place.

and grottoes, corals that grow in tiers like apartment houses and hang in folds like draperies, and corals that sprawl in strange, convoluted masses, lobed and puck- ered like fungus growths.

Only an expert can identify the hundreds of different species that abide in reefs, but in general the dominant reef-building corals separate into two categories: the deli- cate branching forms represented by the staghorn corals; and the solid, unbranched types such as the yellow-green "brain" corals or the gray or bluish Goniopora. Among these the fragile staghorns are incomparably the most beautiful. The tougher brain corals and Goniopora are usually round and boulderlike. Less important, but still common on most coral reefs are: the mushroom coral, a polyp about the size of a dinner plate; Millepore corals, which form yellow bladelike encrustations; soft Alcyona- rian corals which have eight fringed tentacles; and the so- called horny Alcyonarian corals which include the types commonly known as sea whips, sea rods and sea fans.

Among the permanent inhabitants of a coral reef are certain other fixed or sessile creatures such as burrowing mollusks, bryozoans, tunicates and sponges (*lower left*). Yet these are essentially tenants, not proprietors. The corals alone are the hosts, for they are the craftsmen that actually create the crenellated castles of the sea and em- bellish them with magic palettes.

PEACOCK WORMS, a variety of tubeworm, extend their gills to breathe. Their bodies are housed in limy tubes which they build and anchor to coral or sand; only their heads protrude. The gills serve a respiratory function and also convey food down to their clawlike feelers by rippling movements of the "feathers" edging each gill. When alarmed they close their gills like parasols and retract into their tubes.

COLORFUL CREATURES gleam in the shallows of the Atlantic shore. Though looking like flowers, all the objects shown here are animals save for the rockweed at top. The redbeard sponge (*left*) and the speckled sea pork (*center*) are sedentary. Around them crawl a few transients—scarlet starfish, pink anemones (*right*), a gray sea urchin —hardy invertebrates that live in both tropic and temperate waters.

The Invertebrate Visitors

OF all the enclaves of life in the sea, none is more populous than the waters of a coral reef. Here nature creates with an exuberance manifested in no other precinct of the living world. And here, in particular, the humble orders of invertebrates have come into their own, flourishing and producing giants of their kind—starfish a foot in diameter, anemones two feet across, seven-pound oysters and clams that weigh a quarter of a ton.

These invertebrates also transcend others of their kind in the brilliance of their investiture. Species which elsewhere hide in dull attire flaunt gorgeous raiment on coral reefs. Starfish shine in sapphire and scarlet. Tiny shrimps glow with iridescent hues. Painted lobsters promenade in purple and green. Of all these dandies, none is more elegant than the shy and dainty tubeworm (*opposite page*).

A GIANT BLUE STARFISH basks on a coral flat. These Pacific starfish grow up to 12 inches across. To feed, a starfish extrudes its stomach through its mouth; the stomach then envelops and digests the prey.

A DECORATOR CRAB uses a piece of fire sponge, which it holds with its turned up legs, to camouflage itself. Other decorator crabs grow plants on their backs, pruning them when they become too dense.

177

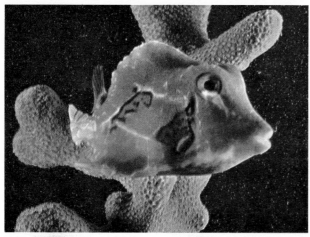

A TRUNKFISH glides stiffly around a coral tree. Unlike other fish which swim with undulating movements of their bodies, the trunkfish has a rigid torso and propels itself with movements of its fins and tail.

The Vertebrate Visitors

THE lagoons, tidal pools and grottoes of a coral reef swarm not only with invertebrates but with myriads of fish more varied than any in the sea. Since clear reef waters contain little plankton, they do not sustain the big edible fish that thrive in colder, nutrient-rich areas of the sea. However, the warm tropic waters of the reefs engender a multiplicity of rare and exotic species.

The four main fish families of the reefs—butterflies, damsels, surgeons and wrasses—are able to subsist as vegetarians when living prey grows scarce. Another sizable family, the parrot fish, actually crunch and swallow coral rock in quest of the algae on which they subsist. Others eat crustaceans and mollusks. Most of the reef fish are small and delicate, but like the invertebrates with which they share the coral world they are splendidly arrayed.

A PARROT FISH is unique among vertebrates of the reef in that it is able to eat the hard encrustations of coral algae. It is equipped with four tough molars, set deep in its throat, that act as a grinding mill.

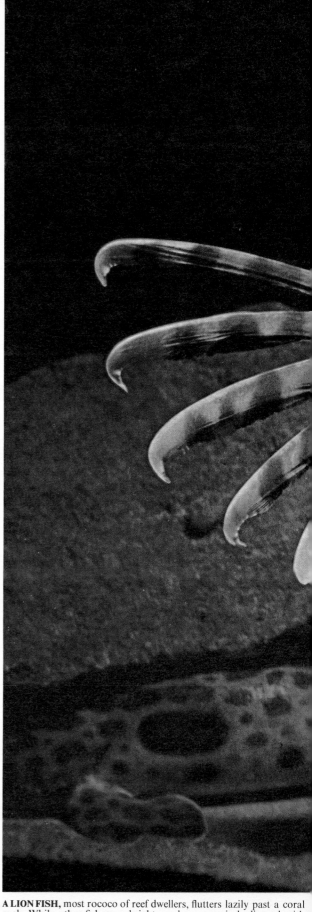

A LION FISH, most rococo of reef dwellers, flutters lazily past a coral rock. While other fish wear brighter colors, none is bedizened with such frills and furbelows as the lion fish with its fanlike, feathered,

fringed dorsal and pectoral fins and dappled tail. For all its splendor, the lion fish is among the most dangerous of the coral reef's inhabitants. It is a cousin of the poisonous Pacific stonefish, deadliest of all marine creatures. Though its venom is less lethal, the lion fish can nevertheless inflict a painful wound on any creature that comes in contact with the sharp, virulent spines that ridge its handsome back.

179

A CONCHFISH seeks security behind the shell of one of the large conch mollusks that creep on coral sands. A very timorous fish, it has pinkish, shiny scales that blend perfectly with the conch's inner lip.

A FROG FISH, camouflaged as an algae-covered coral rock, lies in wait for prey. From its head dangles a rod tipped with a fleshy lure. When smaller fish approach to investigate, the frog fish eats them.

Masters of Camouflage

FROM the standpoint of marine biology, a coral reef is a distinct domain of life, unique in its environment and populations. Yet like all great divisions of the natural world, a coral reef has its own subdivisions, its subsidiary provinces of sand and coral, deep and shallow water, each with its own habitual incumbents.

Thus there are reef fish that live in the lagoons and those that prefer the open sea beyond the reef's walls. The silverside Atherion plays in the surge channels. The dwarf sea bass Pseudochromis lurks in the edges of the coral cliffs. Blennies, gobies and snake eels haunt the coral flats,

Continued on page 184

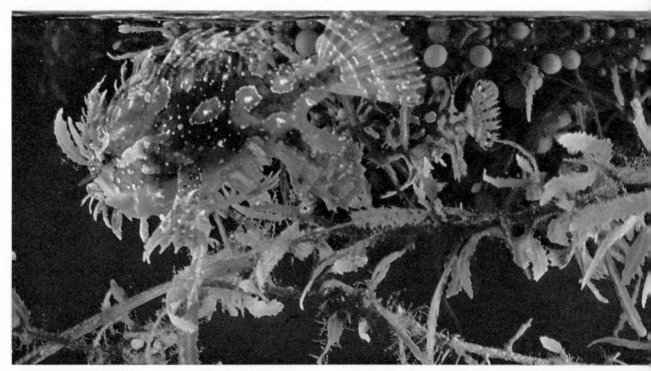

THE SARGASSUM FISH, a voracious carnivore, is virtually indistinguishable from the seaweeds that drift in the Sargasso Sea and the reef waters of the Caribbean. From nose to tail it is embellished with golden-brown tassels, knobs and striated ribbons that simulate the foliage and flotation bladders of the Sargassum weeds, to which it clings with its fins and among whose tangled stalks it hunts its prey.

A SCORPION FISH sits motionless on the bottom, resting on its wing-like fins, waiting for one of the sardines above to blunder within range of its oversized mouth. Its body is embossed and embroidered with a filigree of fleshy protuberances that serve to camouflage it as a sea-weed-bearded coral stone. These threads and wisps also serve as sensory organs that tell the scorpion fish when prey or enemies are near.

181

A BARRACUDA, one of the fiercest and most voracious of fish, will attack anything that moves in the water, including man. Two to eight feet in length, barracudas are swifter, craftier and more courageous than the dull, thick-bodied sharks which also prowl the coral seas. They often lie in wait, motionless, near rocks or coral heads, then dart out with the speed of a javelin to slash the flesh and bone of their prey.

A STING RAY carries on its tail a venomous spike capable of producing paralysis. A bottom dweller, the ray, which camouflages itself with sand, uses its sting not to kill prey but to defend itself against attack.

A MORAY EEL lurks in crannies of coral reefs, waiting for its prey, and will strike savagely at human swimmers who come within range. Sometimes eight feet in length, moray eels can cause serious injury.

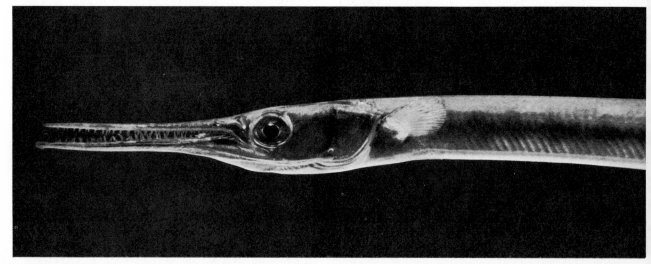

A NEEDLEFISH is armed with beaklike jaws, studded with many fine teeth. Ranging in size from 15 inches to four feet, needlefish are no menace to divers, but they are implacable destroyers of small fish.

A GIANT GROUPER is dangerous, not by disposition but because of its great size and carnivorous appetite. Some attain a length of eight feet, weigh 600 pounds and if hungry could engulf a boy in one bite.

Continued from page 180

burrowing into loose sand to hide when the tide is out. The specialization of reef fish for particular habitats attains its apogee with those that exist in close relationships with other creatures, as, for example, the damselfish which hides among the tentacles of the sea anemone, and the tiny pearl fish, Carapus, which actually makes its home inside the body cavities of sea cucumbers.

Many reef fish have evolved unique physical features in adapting to their chosen ways of life. Thus a species of mullet which feeds in shoal waters has developed fringed lips which serve to keep sand out of its mouth. The needlefish and certain other fish which hunt near the surface of the water have ridges over their eyes to shade them from the sun. The flounders, which lie on their sides on sandy bottoms, are perfectly designed for their individual habitats; the mouth is situated on one side and, even more remarkable, one eye migrates in early life from the downward side to join the other on the upward side.

In the diversified and multicolored world of the coral reef the art of camouflage is more highly developed than in any other domain of nature. Scorpion, Sargassum and frog fishes blend perfectly with their surroundings. Hogfish and groupers change color as they glide past variegated backgrounds. Butterfly fish wear eye-shaped patterns on their tails, possibly to confuse their attackers.

Some reef creatures are further equipped with poison. Among these are certain sea urchins and reef starfish, the sting ray, and the scorpion and lion fish whose poisonous spines cause temporary paralysis. Deadliest of all reef creatures, however, is the stonefish. Upon its slimy, warty back stand 13 erectile spines, each needle-sharp and fed by a pair of venom glands containing a nerve poison for which there is no known antidote.

These virulent fish present the principal perils of coral reefs to man. Yet all are passive. The only other dangerous reef creatures are the active predators that steal in from the open waters—the shark, the barracuda and an occasional giant grouper. Students of reef life do not agree, however, on the degree of aggressiveness of these carnivorous fish. All have been known to attack men and cause injury or death. Yet some naturalists insist that a swimmer is safe so long as he remains under water where the fish can see him, and risks attack only when he splashes about on the surface like a school of frightened herring. Most authorities agree that, unless stimulated by blood in the water, sharks are relatively cautious; a swimmer's best tactic is to swim away as smoothly as he can. Barracudas, however, are utterly savage and without fear. Their monstrous mouths and knifelike teeth can slash an arm or leg to the bone. They are generally the fiercest pirates of the sea.

For the sea contains, insofar as modern man has been able to ascertain, no horned serpents or monsters of ancient myth. Apart from these hungrily predaceous hunters and some poisonous but completely unaggressive creatures the coral reef contains few hazards. Year by year, as naturalists and amateur divers explore its skeleton stone cities, new wonders and new beauties are disclosed, evoking afresh the poet's words, "In chambers deep, Where waters sleep, What unknown treasures pave the floor!"

THE LAND
OF THE SUN

PART IX

THE LAND OF THE SUN

DUNES ROLLING TO THE HORIZONS EPITOMIZE THE DESERT

TODAY there are few blank areas remaining on the maps of the earth and they appear mostly in the Antarctic. Yet many misconceptions about the earth persist; among these one of the most stubborn overhangs the 10 million square miles of desert. Popular fancy continues to envisage a desert as a cruel, inimical expanse of shifting sands. But this is a fragmentary representation, applicable to only a small portion of desert. Less than 30% of the Sahara consists of sand dunes; only 2% of the deserts of North America are overspread with dunes. In most desert regions plants grow, animals prosper and some rain descends.

Although differing widely in climate and conformation, all deserts, wherever they exist—whether they are hot like those of central Australia or cold like the Gobi—share certain aspects. They are lands of the sky—an enormous, overpowering sky. Beneath its implacable glare colors efface themselves; the world appears painted in pastel hues—soft tans, gray-greens and dull, muted reds. Hills and mountains stand forth bold and austere. Dry riverbeds furrow the eroded hills, crease the desert flats and vanish in the cracked mud of empty lakes. From time to time winds race across the open plain, driving yellow clouds of dust aloft. By day the great ineluctable fact of the desert is the sun. By night it is the purple bowl of the heavens, sequined with innumerable stars.

Authorities do not agree on the precise geographical boundaries which delineate the deserts of the earth—where, for example, a semiarid region ends and a desert begins. Meteorologists have long cited as deserts those regions where evaporation exceeds precipitation. Botanists envisage them as regions of widely spaced and peculiarly specialized vegetation. And geologists describe them in terms of land forms, erosion cycles and interior drainage systems. A common rule of thumb defines them as areas with an annual rainfall of less than 10 inches. For all the arguing over definition, the outstanding attribute of all deserts is dryness. And from this one basic quality stem all the other characteristics—botanical, zoological, geological—that make deserts what they are.

Although the word desert means, literally, a deserted or uninhabited place, the connotation is misleading. For the deserts have their populations—a host of small, burrowing creatures many of which are uniquely endowed with an ability to go through life without drinking water. And along with these unusual animals dwell similarly specialized plants. Many bear thorns and other defenses. Many have tiny leaves or no leaves at all. Yet they are plants and they are green and they flourish in the parched desert soil.

Contrary to popular opinion, the desert, though dry, is not completely dry. Some rain falls from time to time, though it is so meager, irregular and undependable that permanent lakes and streams cannot exist. Occasionally, however, a sudden downpour will fill the dried drainage systems of the desert with rushing torrents that roar down the parched canyons for perhaps an hour or two and then sink without trace into the insatiable earth.

Although in most of the world's deserts the relative humidity is extremely low throughout the year, as in every domain of nature there are paradoxes. The coastal

TO MAN. BUT IN FACT DUNES COVER BUT A FRACTION OF THE EARTH'S ARID LANDS. THESE STAND IN THE SONORAN DESERT

deserts of South America and Africa, for example, are "fog deserts"; they have high humidity, clouds and mists, but virtually no rain. The Sahara, on the other hand, shows a cloud cover of only 10% during the winter and less than 4% from June to October. As a corollary, deserts are the hottest places on earth. The highest temperature ever officially recorded was taken in the Sahara at Azizia, Libya: 136° in the shade. The U.S. record is not much lower: 134° at Death Valley, Calif. Yet, owing to their low humidity, deserts are subject to great ranges of temperature, both diurnally and seasonally. Such middle latitude deserts as the Gobi and Takla Makan of Asia experience both scorching summers and freezing winters,

with blizzards and wild subzero winds out of the Siberian wastes to the north.

The deserts that stipple the visage of the planet today did not exist always. Most of them evolved concurrently with the uplifting of the earth's highest mountain ranges during the last 15 million years. Today they form a distinct pattern, girdling the globe in two great belts above and below the equator in latitudes approximately 15° to 40° north and south (*see map, page 189*). Their distribution on the earth's surface reflects the physical factors that created them. Many complex agencies contribute to the formation of a desert, and it is seldom that the pattern of their interweaving is repeated. One feature com-

187

mon to most deserts is their location in the western portions of continents wherever warm, dry, descending air dissipates the cloud cover and allows more sunlight to reach and heat the land. Another obvious but inadequate factor is the rain-shadow effect of mountain ranges. It is evident that just as some of the rainiest regions of the earth lie on the windward side of mountains, so some of its most arid areas are situated in their lee.

Yet mountain barriers alone cannot explain the intensely dry coastal deserts of Chile and Peru. Here the factor of ocean currents becomes important, for when cold currents parallel a coast, an anomalous combination of fog and aridity may be produced. In this case the Peru Current, which flows northward from the Antarctic, cools breezes from the Pacific, causing condensation and creating a heavy fog. And when the chilled and misty air reaches the land, it is warmed and its moisture capacity is thereby increased; and so, though the fog blows inland, it dissipates rapidly and seldom resolves into rain. The city of Lima, for example, has an annual rainfall of two inches, though it is often enshrouded in melancholy mists. And the adjacent Atacama Desert, with a precipitation average of less than .5 inch a year, is the world's driest desert—though it is but a few miles from the sea.

Virtually all these factors affect America's Sonoran Desert, whose various aspects are illustrated in this essay as archetypal of deserts. Coastal ranges of California and Mexico shadow its inland reaches from rain-bearing winds from the Pacific. The cold California Current influences its coastal sections, creating typical fog-desert conditions along the peninsula of Baja California. Its interior is bathed by dry, descending air. Though smaller by far, the Sonoran Desert presents an analogue of the Sahara. In some respects it is peculiarly American. But its elemental land forms—its bald, eroded mountains, its flats, alluvial fans and dunes, its parched riverbeds and waterless lakes—are features of the greater desert world.

From above, by day, the golden sun glares down with the same unblinking eye that scans the haunted wastes of Asia. By night the Milky Way streams across the firmament and the stars burn with the same intensity that bemused the Alexandrian astronomers of 2,000 years ago. In every direction across its vast, flat and clean expanses there flow glassy rivers of pellucid space.

NORTH AMERICA'S DESERTS are situated in the western portion of the U.S. and the northern part of Mexico shown above, mostly in rugged country where high coastal ranges effectively shadow their depressed basins from moisture-laden winds from the sea. Although geographers recognize four separate deserts in this generally arid region, their boundaries are not everywhere distinct. This map focuses

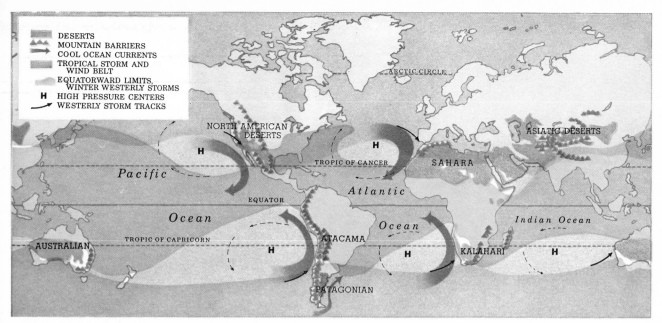

DESERTS OF THE WORLD, deployed in two globe-girdling bands, lie generally between the moist mid-latitude westerlies and the equatorial rainy belt. Often they occur in the west of continents where dry winds, circling offshore highs, sweep parallel to the shore, creating mist over cold currents, but carrying little rain inland. Asiatic desert areas are created by distance from the sea and encircling mountains.

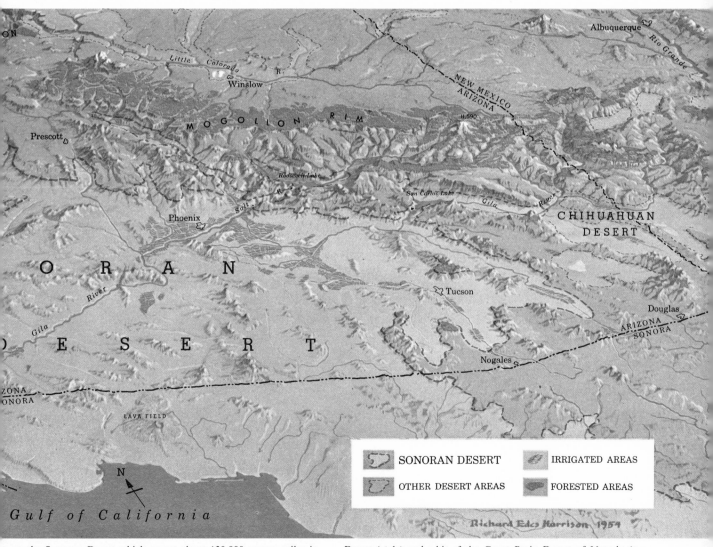

on the Sonoran Desert which covers about 120,000 square miles in sections of the U.S. and Mexico surrounding the Gulf of California. Also visible are the Mojave Desert, an extension of the Chihuahuan Desert (*right*) and a bit of the Great Basin Desert of Nevada (*top left*). The Sonoran is generally the most extreme, though Death Valley holds U.S. records for high temperature and minimum rainfall.

189

THE EDGE OF THE DESERT in this view of the Laguna escarpment is clearly defined by the coastal climate of the western slopes (*foreground*) and the arid climate in the rain shadow to the east.

The Desert Countenance

PARADOXICALLY the architect and sculptor of the harsh desert landscape is running water. Sparse and infrequent though they are, desert rains descend with torrential violence, creating wild streams which rush down the barren flanks of mountains, unhindered by trees or soil, and bite deeply into the rock, carving it into sharp, angular forms. And as they erode they transport sediment, piling it up at the foot of the mountains in gently sloping bajadas or alluvial fans. Spreading over the desert flats, these streams create their own drainage channels. Sometimes, when the underlying rock is soft, they dissect the land into a maze of narrow canyons and knife-edge ridges known as badlands (*left, below*).

But unlike the streams of humid lands they seldom reach the sea. For the drainage pattern of desert regions is an internal one. The swift flood waters that pour briefly down their scorched beds end up eventually in closed basins where they form temporary lakes or playas. Some playas remain moist, with water tables only a foot or two below the surface or even with a shallow brackish layer of water above the floor. But more disappear, leaving a surface that quickly anneals and cracks in the hot sun (*left, above*). Few plants can grow on these dry lakes, but around their edges a few green rings of saltbush and mesquite subsist.

Usually no more than a fifth of the vast, level expanse of the desert flats is covered with vegetation. For the rest, there are only vistas of mingled sand and gravel, or naked rock. Where sands are exposed to persistent winds, dunes may form. More widespread than dunes are areas where coarse fragments of rocks have been laid down by water and planed by winds. In the Sahara and other arid regions of the ancient world, though not in North America, broad stretches of the underlying bedrock called *hammadas* lie exposed to the sky.

Here and there, amid the most forbidding of desert wastelands, an occasional emerald oasis glistens in the wilderness as a reminder of the persistence of life. For underground water may sometimes emerge from alluvial fans or seep to the surface in isolated pockets and basins; and wherever fresh water exists, plants will grow.

A DRY LAKE, or playa, lies in a valley in the Sonoran Desert. The flat, cracked floors of playas are often found in desert landscapes. Below: the Borrego badlands reveal the sculpture of violent desert rains.

AN OASIS flourishes around a snow-fed stream in a canyon of Mt. San Jacinto in the Sonoran Desert. Any green or fertile place in the desert is an oasis, whatever the source of water. The flood plains of the Nile and Colorado rivers are vast oases, and so are arid areas irrigated by man. Here water has enabled fan palms to grow. Also common in American oases are cottonwoods, desert willows, rushes and tules.

GIANT SAGUARO CACTI, which may grow 50 feet tall, are the water towers of the Sonoran Desert. Their expandable, corrugated trunks store hundreds of gallons of rain soaked up and transported to them after infrequent storms by a network of far-reaching surface roots. Birds often peck nest holes in the pulpy trunks, which the saguaros line with a gourdlike shell to prevent further loss of precious moisture.

YUCCA ROOTS, shown partially exposed (*above*), hold enough water to enable the plants to flourish in the Sonoran Desert. Water is also stored in the leaves, which have a waxy coating to curtail evaporation.

MESQUITE ROOTS bore 30 or more feet into a wash in the Sonoran Desert to drink water (*right*). A young mesquite will restrict its growth above ground until its root has located an adequate water supply.

A KANGAROO RAT leaps to evade a striking king snake. Like most desert carnivores this snake requires moist flesh to fill his water needs. The kangaroo rat can subsist on dry seeds alone.

Animals of the Waterless World

SINCE water is the basis of life, composing the greater part of the tissues of all living things, the crucial problem of desert animals is to survive in a world where sources of flowing water are rare. Many pass their entire lives without a single drop.

Uncompromising as it is, the desert has not eliminated life but only those forms unable to withstand its desiccating effects. Its populations are largely nocturnal, silent, filled with reticence and ruled by stealth. But having adapted to their austere environment, they are as healthy as animals anywhere on earth.

The secret of their adjustment lies in a combination of behavior and physiology. Most pass the burning hours asleep in cool, humid burrows underneath the ground, emerging to hunt only by night. The surface of the sun-baked desert averages around 150°, but 18 inches down the temperature is only 60°.

The herbivores find water in desert plants; the carnivores slake their thirst with flesh and blood. One of the most remarkable adjustments, however, has been made by the tiny kangaroo rat (*above*), who not only lives without drinking but subsists on a diet of dry seeds. He has the ability to manufacture water in his body by the metabolic conversion of carbohydrates and conserves his small supply by every possible means, expending only minuscule amounts in his excreta and through evaporation from his respiratory tract.

Given these endowments, man might be the most successful of desert animals, for he can subject himself to sustained activity in temperatures that would kill other creatures. But his very capacity for this is the consequence of his delicate heat-regulating system. Man's body is a water-cooled engine. In extreme heat he may lose as much as a quart an hour by perspiration. Without water he could live only two or three days at a temperature of 100°. At 120° he might not last a day.

DESERT MULE DEER convene by night at a water hole. Most creatures of the desert drink when water is at hand. But whether deer are drawn to oases for the water or for their vegetation is not known.

PECCARY grub in the damp mud at the base of a spiny cholla. The only native American wild pig, the peccary has omnivorous tastes and a hearty appetite: it will eat anything from snakes to cactus.

A PACK RAT makes a meal of prickly pear. Like most cactus plants the prickly pear is extremely succulent: 90% of its weight consists of water. For the pack rat it effectively resolves all water problems.

A BOBCAT devours a ground squirrel which provides him with both ➔ food and drink. A versatile beast, the bobcat is at home in both swamps and woodlands, and has also adapted himself to the desert.

A ROAD-RUNNER, a bird that can fly only short distances, attacks a favored item of his diet—a sidewinder rattler, curled in a pad. Should the road-runner not be able to swallow all of his moisture-giving meal at once, he may go about with the unconsumed part dangling from his long beak and digest it inch by inch. Road-runners have bristle-tipped topknots, jauntily elevated tail feathers and a clownlike gait.

A BANDED GECKO, a nocturnal lizard of the desert, has beady eyes that allow him to see in the dark, but he is not as sinister as he looks. He is only four inches long and eats only insects, which he pounces on.

A SIDEWINDER RATTLESNAKE of the American Southwest travels broadside across the desert with a looping motion which leaves an S-shaped track. This motion cuts down contact with the hot sands.

CHUCKWALLA
SPOTTED SKUNK
PACK RAT
COLLARED LIZARD
GILA MONSTER
WHITE-FOOTED MOUSE
CACTUS WREN
JACK RABBIT
ANTELOPE GROUND SQUIRREL   LECONTE'S THRASHER
BULL SNAK

The Desert by Day

AS dawn breaks over the Sonoran Desert, the diurnal animals begin to stir. By 9 a.m. the day's activities are under way. The painting on these pages encompasses life above and below the ground at this particular hour and illustrates two kinds of desert terrain—a bajada slope (*left*) with its coarse soil and giant saguaros, yellow-green paloverde trees, flame-tipped deerhorn chollas, barrel cactus, teddybear cactus and prickly pears; and a desert flat

(*right*) with its finer soil and mottling of green creosote bushes and bur sage.

The first creatures to arise are the birds. High temperatures are fatal to them and they must feed either early in the morning or late in the afternoon. Some make their homes inside the thick, moisture-laden columns of the giant saguaros. The cactus wren establishes his fortress among the fierce, impregnable spines of the cholla. Some birds fly long distances in quest of springs or pools. But most of them, like Leconte's thrasher and Gambel's quail, fulfill their needs with berries, seeds, insects and

RING-TAILED CAT   HORNED OWL

CHUCKWALLA   PACK RAT   SPOTTED SKUNK

            ANTELOPE GROUND SQUIRREL   BULL SNAKE   DESERT TORTOISE

The Desert by Night

BY evening the unending battles of hunter and hunted are raging underneath the stars. Snug in their secret strongholds, the creatures of the day lie sleeping.

In the grim food chain of the desert nearly every creature represents a meal for others larger than itself. At the bottom of the hierarchy stand the rodents. They provide food for all. Yet they too must eat. The pack rat, having dined on cactus, mesquite leaves and prickly pear, pro-

ceeds, oblivious of his fate, with his obsessive occupation of adding litter to his nest. His cousin, the white-footed mouse, also lives dangerously, for though he can subsist on vegetation, he sometimes risks his life to get insects and spiders. A more distant relative, the kangaroo rat, is a hoarder too, but he is extremely agile, capable of leaping high in the air. The kangaroo rat is a tasty morsel, enjoyed by virtually every carnivore on the desert flats. His close kin, the pocket mouse, is almost equally in demand.

Less vulnerable than the mice, but still a fugitive, is the black-tailed jack rabbit, capable of speed up to 45 mph

FOLD OUT, DO NOT TEAR

his tail and, leaving it behind to fascinate the foe, escapes and grows a new one.

Apart from the birds and lizards, the desert animals are generally nocturnal (*following pages*). Two notable reptilian exceptions are the bull snake and the tortoise. The jack rabbit may appear in early morning but often as not will seek the shade later. Only the playful ground squirrels and the peccary may still be active as the sun climbs toward the zenith.

Meanwhile, all day long, another population has lain dormant, sleeping away the bright hours. Some of its members, like the spotted skunk and the poisonous Gila monster, slumber in rock cavities. The pack rat enjoys security in his shallow trench overlain with cactus pads, plant litter and other debris. The coyote, who has few enemies save man, dozes in the shade of a creosote bush. The badger suns himself in the mouth of his burrow. The sidewinder rattlesnake coils himself in a flattened pad, sometimes—if the heat is not too great—in the open sand. But there are also many less audacious creatures asleep under the ground—the kangaroo rat, the white-footed mouse, the pocket mouse and the shy kit fox.

PECCARY

DESERT TORTOISE

BADGER

SIDEWINDER
POCKET MOUSE

COYOTE

DESERT IGUANA

spiders. Predaceous birds obtain sufficient moisture from the bodies of their prey. The turkey vulture circles in the flaming sky, scanning the desert for the carrion that will provide his dinner. On the ground the swift road-runner sprints across the flats, topknot bobbing, in hot pursuit of juicy snakes and lizards. And among the branches of a creosote bush the shrike impales his living prey upon a twig and leaves it there for future reference.

The lizards are by and large diurnal animals, though cold-blooded and extremely sensitive to heat. Even the beady-eyed chuckwalla, who reputedly suns himself on rocks too hot for man to touch, can stand only a few minutes' exposure before retreating to his cool crevice in the rocks. The chuckwalla is a vegetarian; the collared lizard is not only carnivorous but cannibalistic; and the horned lizard (often misnamed horned toad) loves ants. In the matter of defense the lizards are also diversified. The gridiron-tailed lizard relies on speed, making as much as 15 miles per hour. The chuckwalla's defense when in peril is to squeeze himself into a rock crevice and inflate himself with air, thus making it impossible to pull him out. The desert iguana, when seized from behind, sheds

and leaps as long as 15 feet. Essentially a vegetarian, fond of succulent plants and the bark of shrubs, the jack is active day and night, for his appetite is large. Intermediate in the food chain is the spotted skunk—at once predator and prey. Omnivorous, his diet includes cactus fruits, crickets, grasshoppers and at times carrion. But he is also a flesh-eater, a fancier of mice and baby rabbits. Livelier and smaller than his cousin, the familiar striped skunk, he possesses the same chemical armament, plus a trick of standing on his hands in moments of peril to confuse his enemies. He has a number of foes, among them

the horned owl, whose soft plumage renders his flight completely noiseless.

Certain poisonous reptiles also haunt the desert flats by night. One of the few nocturnal lizards is the Gila monster. Docile and slow-moving, he does not bite unless provoked. His favorite food consists of quail eggs, young rabbits and ground squirrels. Vastly more dangerous and aggressive are the desert rattlesnakes: the diamondback, an irritable predator, averaging about 3½ feet in length, who comes forth at night in quest of rodents, birds and rabbits; and the sidewinder, a smaller but no

POCKET MOUSE   KIT FOX   BOBCAT   BADGER

less active reptile with a unique method of locomotion that carries him broadside across the sands.

The aristocrats of the night are the larger mammals. Perhaps the most curious is the shrewd ring-tailed cat. Agile, inquisitive, strictly nocturnal, he appears on the desert floor late at night. His favorite food is the pack rat. The shy kit fox is the special connoisseur of kangaroo rats. Scarcely larger than a house cat, the kit fox can run for short distances at incredible speed and succumbs to few antagonists. One is the bobcat, a sly hunter and ferocious fighter. Another confident and relatively independ-

ent hunter is the badger. Endowed with powerful front feet and long claws, he lives boldly in open places where he can excavate the homes of rodents. The best known of desert animals, and monarch of the flats, however, is the handsome, lean coyote. A versatile hunter, he can stalk and dig with equal success.

As the bright banners of dawn unfurl across the sky, one of the last creatures to retire is the little western bat who hunts moths and other insects. Folding his leathery wings, he crawls into a narrow crevice in the rocks to slumber away the day.

A WIND-SHEARED BUSH in San Gorgonio Pass attests the abrasive power of the desert wind. Blowing uphill with force, the wind has pruned the shrub in line with the top of the rock that shelters it.

Cutting Wind and Savage Sun

THE clear and lucent air that overhangs the desert is sullied from time to time by clouds of dust and sand. Winds ride unbridled across the barren flats, and with them rides fierce sand, blasting objects in its path. The finer particles of dust spiral aloft, diffusing in opaque clouds that dim the sun until the caprice of the wind sets them down on other landscapes far away.

The desert air is often troubled too on windless days by the influence of the sun. Heated by the blaze of noon, the atmospheric layer closest to the ground may form a refracting layer that bends light waves from above, producing inverse images and reflecting the blue ocean of the sky. From this effect originates the mirage—blue lakes and rivers shimmering in the arid wilderness.

A WATER-MIRAGE (*below*) shimmers above a dry lake in Mexico. It is caused by a thin layer of hot air near the ground on which the sky is reflected. Here vegetation appears to be reflected upon the "lake."

A DUST STORM (*above*) sweeps across the Arizona desert, filling the air with clouds of choking particles. With little vegetation to slow its course, the desert wind can lift dust aloft until the sun is darkened.

Dust storms differ from sandstorms, whose heavier particles move across the desert in a low cloud with a clearly defined upper boundary. Dust is so fine that a strong wind can carry it up thousands of feet.

A SUMMER THUNDERSTORM expends its fury on the Arizona desert, lashing the cactus-covered flats with wind, water and hail. Such savage downpours take place mainly in midsummer when seasonal changes in wind and pressure systems bring moist tongues of air in from the Gulf of Mexico. Some of these reach southern Arizona where low pressure centers tend to form over the desert as a conse-

A PILLAR OF RAIN slants out of a distant thunderhead. It is at the base of such columns that deluges like that in the picture at top occur. Rain will bring leaves to the naked ocotillo in the foreground.

When the Rains Come

IN general desert rains originate from two seasonal sources: cyclonic storms borne by the westerlies in winter and local thunderstorms in summer. Yet they are so capricious that in one place none will fall for years; others may receive a year's supply in one swift deluge. Since desert storms are often local, moistening a few square miles at most, regional averages are meaningless. The Sahara, for example, is said to average a little under five inches annually. Yet at Dakhla no rain fell for 11 years.

When they arrive, the rains often descend in brief but torrential downpours. As they hit the bone-dry ground, the baked surface at first sheds them as indifferently as asphalt paving. The accumulating waters may then run off in sheets across the sun-baked flats or pour through deep canyons in wild, turbulent cataracts. Supercharged with mud, sweeping debris before them, they rush furiously down the steeply graded washes, tearing, destroying, eroding until, captured by myriad minute pores in the soil, they seep into the ground or find their way ultimately to some waiting playa. A few hours later nothing will remain but damp mud, cracking in the desert sun.

quence of the intense heating of the land. Crossing the hot sands, the lower portions of the moist air masses are warmed and spiral upward, creating towering thunderheads which occasionally explode into lightning and rain. During such downpours the water descends in nearly solid sheets, and hailstones bombard the flats. Winter rains, arriving principally from the Pacific, are more general and prolonged.

A **FLASH FLOOD** covers the channel of a bajada slope with sheets of turbulent water. Desert drainage is so swift that the run-off from tributary rivulets can produce a rampaging torrent in only half an hour.

A **DAY LATER** the same wash channel shown in the photograph at left appears virtually dry, save for a few patches of mud. Baked by the sun's rays, it will soon look as desiccated as the flats surrounding it.

SAGUARO BLOSSOMS appear atop the ordinarily bald summits of the giant cactus during May, capping its spiny stalks incongruously with delicate waxy blooms. The saguaro blossom is Arizona's state flower.

HEDGEHOG CACTUS BLOSSOMS adorn the foot-high, branched cactus on which they grow. Brightening rocky ledges of the Arizona desert, the hedgehog's blooms are forerunners of its juicy, edible fruit.

MARIPOSA LILIES touch the flats with flame. Among the loveliest of Southwestern flowers, the Mariposa lily is a perennial. Its bulb lives through drought, while the plant dies back, blooming again after rain.

And the Desert Blossoms

FOR all their brevity and violence, the desert rains do not invariably vanish without effect. The year-round desert plants have ways of utilizing sudden downpours. Many cacti have spreading root systems that are able to absorb quantities of water in a single rainstorm and thick, expansible stems that can store it for many arid months. Other plants, like the paloverde, conserve water by resorting to minute leaves in order to reduce the amount lost by transpiration. Still others, like the ocotillo, survive prolonged dry spells by shedding their leaves entirely, or like the brittlebush, by letting whole branches die back, while keeping their roots alive.

But the desert has other equally remarkable plants. These are the ephemerals or flowering annuals. Unlike the cacti and other drought-resistant plants, the ephemerals lie dormant through the dry periods of the calendar. Then astonishingly, after a freshening rain, they germinate, flower and bear seeds—all in six to eight weeks. These short-lived ephemerals are among the most prolific of desert plants, representing almost half of the vegetation of the Sonoran region. Swift to blossom, swift to die, they paint the landscape briefly with bright, magic colors, fulfilling for a time the ancient prophecy, "And the desert shall rejoice, and blossom as the rose."

BARREL CACTUS BLOSSOMS crown the bristly stem of their parent plant. The tough, springy spines of this well-known cactus were used by Indians for fishhooks. Blooms usually appear in March and April.

SPRING REVEILLE of rains makes the desert sands come alive with color. During the dry season seeds of flowering annuals lie dormant. After rain, they swiftly germinate and flower, transfiguring the somber landscape with their gaudy pigments. Here in the Coachella Valley the wan green of the perennials is spangled with yellow desert dandelions, white evening primroses and purple clusters of fragrant sand verbena.

ALTHOUGH the deserts of the earth, covering about 19% of the planetary land surface, sustain only 5% of its population, they encompass far more than wasteland. Under their shifting scarves of sun-seared sand and soil lie many of the earth's richest resources—the diamonds of Africa's Namib Desert and the oil of Arabia and Iran. The vast nitrate deposits of Chile's Atacama Desert and the borax of the Mojave owe their very existence to lack of rainfall. For nitrate, gypsum, borax and other valuable salts are water-soluble substances that would be leached out and borne away to the sea in regions of more abundant precipitation and exterior drainage.

Long before man ever uncovered these hidden riches, however, he wrested some food from the desert soil by regulating the limited water supplies at hand. The Egyptians were among the first to develop the art of watering the desert, for the periodic flooding of the Nile, alternating with long periods of drought, suggested the control of water flow by dikes, canals and dams. Other ancient civilizations also practiced desert irrigation. The Tigris and Euphrates supplied water to the Sumerians, Babyloni-ans and Assyrians. The Indus River supported an early culture in India. Indeed it is thought that agriculture first flourished in irrigated regions, like these river floodplains whose open tracts were easier to cultivate than the tangled forests and stubbly grasslands of more favorable climes. Desert soils, though deficient in humus, are often rich in other plant foods; and the perennial sunshine may engender two or three crops a year. Some of the richest farmland in the world lies in the irrigated Imperial Valley of the Sonoran Desert.

In many ways man has conquered the desert. He has punctured its parched surface with oil wells and mines, spanned it with roads and flown above it in planes. Yet, like the oceans and lofty mountain ranges of the earth, the desert remains among the great barriers of the planet's surface, dividing mankind and repelling human encroachments. Though here and there man has occupied its scattered green oases, he has barely dotted the vast antipathetic expanses that roll to the empty horizons, as they have for centuries, mile after burning mile, barren, implacable, a "sea-like, pathless, limitless waste."

Volume 3, which completes *The World We Live In,* portrays life in the arctic barrens, in the tropical rain forest and in the woodlands of our own temperate zones. It also describes the universe beyond the planet Earth. The final volume includes a bibliography for further reading and a comprehensive index for all three volumes.